Complete Story by H.R. TOFT

Once Upon A Fairy Tale

... there was a handsome "prince" who fell for a beautiful "princess" — but their love story took two generations to reach a happy ending.

ONE of the best friends I ever had was my grandfather. He would bounce me on his bony knees and smile down at me with twinkling, grey eyes.

I can never remember him raising his voice except when he laughed and then the whole house would echo with great rollicking guffaws. Which brought a mild reproach from my mother.

Saturday night was the time I looked forward to more than any other. My parents always went out and I was allowed to stay up an extra half-hour with my grandfather.

An elastic half-hour, because Grandpa could always be persuaded to tell me about the music box.

"Tell me a story, Grandpa. Tell me about the music box."

"Oh," he would say, pulling at his moustache. "And how many times have you heard that story before?"

"Please, Grandpa?"

He would regard me gravely for a moment. Then his face would dissolve into a thousand leathery wrinkles and he would pull my ear gently. "Robin, me boy," he'd say. "You've a tongue as wheedlin' as your mother's."

He didn't need much persuading, though. All the time he'd be fingering the key which hung from his watch chain. The key which opened the old wooden trunk which always sat in the corner of our spacious kitchen.

5

ONCE UPON A FAIRY TALE

Lifting me from his knee, he would amble over to the trunk.

The music box was always buried deep among the mysterious contents of that chest. But he would find it, and carry it tenderly, as if it was the most sacred treasure in the world, back to his chair.

"Solid silver, my boy," were his first words.

"Play it, Grandpa. Please!"

With a gnarled finger he would probe underneath the box and I would hold my breath as the delicate, tinkling notes filled the kitchen. It was the sweetest music I'd ever heard.

Then the box would be placed into my hands and I'd hold it tightly. This was the moment I enjoyed most, when Grandpa trusted me with his precious music box.

The story would come then. A story no-one else, I'm sure, was ever told. Only a child would have understood.

It always started off as a fairy story. Grandpa saw himself as a prince. And Elizabeth was the fair princess.

"She was the most beautiful princess there has ever been. Her hair was as fair as gossamer gleaming in the golden sun. Her eyes were more blue than the summer sky, her cheeks were softer than a rose petal.

"When she laughed the world laughed, too. When she frowned the world wept . . .

"The moment the prince saw her, he fell in love with her. But he never thought that she would fall in love with him."

"He went to church and prayed, didn't he?" I interrupted softly.

"Yes, he went to church and prayed that nothing would cause his princess unhappiness and that nothing would ever part them."

"The music box —" I would prompt, impatiently.

"It was lying on a velvet cushion in a shop window. The princess liked it so much they went into the shop to buy it. But the prince was only a poor prince. When he was told how much it cost he knew he couldn't buy it."

"But the princess bought it, didn't she?"

"She went back the following day. You see, the prince didn't know then that she was a very rich princess. The shopkeeper told her that there were two music boxes, exactly alike.

"He wanted Elizabeth to buy them both, saying that bad luck would come to the person who only possessed one.

"But the princess laughed and bought only the one in the window. She took it home and her only regret was that she couldn't tell the prince, because she knew how proud he was."

Here Grandpa would pause for a long time, his mind reaching back to his youth, living again the fairy story which I realised, as I grew older, had been a reality.

But unlike most fairy stories, this one didn't have a happy ending.

I never prompted him at this point. I knew the ending as well as he did and it saddened me. And yet I had to hear it.

ONCE UPON A FAIRY TALE

You see, Elizabeth's parents found out about Grandpa — that he was from a poor family. They sent her away thinking that they would soon forget about each other.

But Grandpa didn't forget. He'd set his heart on buying the music box so that when Elizabeth returned he could present it to her.

He saved and scraped and pinched every penny until at last he had enough money. He didn't find out then that there were two music boxes.

Elizabeth returned a year later. She was married.

Her parents had forced her to marry a wealthy Austrian. And such was the rigid social pressure of her class in those days, that, though she had fought with tears of bitterness and anger, the forces against her were too strong.

Grandpa and she met surreptitiously just twice after that.

At the first meeting Elizabeth pleaded with Grandpa to take her away with him. But, even though every word he uttered tore a piece out of his heart, he refused to consider it, for now she was a married woman.

They met for the last time in the park. In the windswept darkness they exchanged their music boxes as parting gifts. Through her tears Elizabeth whispered, "Perhaps they will come together in an age when people are more enlightened . . ."

* * * *

I was just 10 years old when I heard that story for the last time. I remember that night most vividly.

Instead of sending me to bed as usual, Grandpa replaced the music box in his trunk then unhooked the key from his watch chain.

He pressed it into my hand and I noticed for the first time how tired his eyes were.

"Robin," he said, "I want you to look after this key for me."

But when my parents returned that night his twinkling eyes were stilled. Quietly, without fuss, he had left us for good. I cried for days.

I've never missed anyone as much as I missed my grandfather. But I was young and as the years passed the memory became less poignant. The music box was never forgotten but, as time passed, it was lifted less often from the huge old trunk.

FROM my early days the grace and beauty of well-designed buildings had attracted me. It seemed quite natural that I ended up as an architect.

After I qualified I tried to get as much experience as possible. Any commission that aroused my interest I would accept, no matter how trifling.

So when a friend asked me to take on the renovation of an 18th-century manor house, which belonged to a distant relative of his, I decided to take a look at it.

Continued on page 10

Meet-A-Pet

Here's our selection of some of your favourite pet pictures.

■ Hamish, the West Highland Terrier, just loves getting out in the snow, says owner T. Butler of Glasgow.

■ Mac just loves getting his photo taken, says proud owner J. Parker of London.

■ On cold winter nights, Chloe likes nothing better than lazing about in front of a warm fire. This delightful pic was sent in by Chloe's owner, F. Riddell of Cardiff.

■ Joe, the Border Collie, likes going for walks with his owner's daughter, says Mrs Crofter of Manchester.

■ Loving owner P. Russel says Frankie and Bess are the best of friends.

Our Little Angel

While soft snow whispers on the ground,
From little Jamie there's no sound,
His eyes are closed, he's fast asleep,
So peaceful in his dreams so deep,
He's dreaming of the day ahead,
When he'll jump wide awake from bed,
And find that Christmas Day has come,
The day he'll spend with Dad and Mum,
And George and Jo and Auntie Jan,
And Grampa Pete and Pop and Nan.

While the moon a watchful eye does keep,
From little Jamie there's not a peep,
Sleep softly darling little boy,
For to our hearts you bring such joy,
He's peaceful now, but wait and see,
In the morning what a change there'll be,
His happy voice will fill the air,
And laughter will be everywhere,
But for now this moment we will keep,
Our sweetest boy, our angel asleep.
T. Ashby

ONCE UPON A FAIRY TALE

Continued from page 7

The house was in Norfolk and I loved it at first sight. The owner, a bluff, retired Army officer, soon dampened my enthusiasm however. He wanted the building made smaller, closing off some of the rooms.

"Much too big," he complained. "Costs a fortune to run and there's only my daughter and myself now."

The job was hardly what I'd been led to believe but the house was so delightful I took it on.

Several weeks elapsed before I was able to return with some rough plans. The owner was away but he'd given me carte blanche to go ahead with the alterations.

In fact, there was no-one around but the maid, who had instructions to allow me the run of the house. And it was such a fascinating house, I loved to wander round it.

The interior was that rare mixture of Queen Anne and Georgian architecture. As I climbed the central staircase of solid oak I would pretend I was an 18th-century lord. Now if my grandfather had only married Elizabeth . . .

The train of thought both saddened and intrigued me. I had not thought of my grandfather and his "fairy story" for a long time.

I had never yearned to be an aristocrat — I'd just fallen completely in love with the house.

How could such a lovely place be carved up without losing its essential elegance? The more I inspected the building the more convinced I became that I'd made a mistake in accepting this job. After all, my work was to create, not destroy.

There was one more room which had so far escaped my investigation. I had left it to the last because it was the biggest bedroom, which

10

overlooked the front of the house.

Now I gingerly opened the door and entered — and found myself staring in some astonishment at a silver music box which stood in the centre of the solid oak dressing-table.

I gazed at it for some time, lost in wonder, before I could bring myself to pick it up. It was the twin of the one I had at home.

The delicate tracings on the lid were unmistakable. Every line on the patterned silver was the same. I lifted the lid, knowing before I did that to hear the tinkling music I would need to wind it up. I probed underneath and found the key.

The music box at home played "Oranges And Lemons". The one my grandfather had given Elizabeth played the old song, "Greensleeves".

Yet I couldn't turn the key, couldn't face the possibility of not hearing "Greensleeves". As I stood there, lost in timeless memory, I heard again the words Elizabeth had whispered to my grandfather as they had exchanged the music boxes before parting for ever. "Perhaps they will come together in an age when people are more enlightened . . ." Inwardly, I sighed.

Coincidence, my reason argued. But was it coincidence? Would it still be coincidence if the music box played the tune I so wanted to hear?

I turned the key.

*　　*　　*　　*

Two hours later I was home, and, within minutes after that, driving back to Norfolk with the music box from my grandfather's trunk.

Logic had deserted me now. Pressing me on was a force beyond reason, a force I could not resist. Nor did I want to. I was in the middle of a fairy story that was coming back to life. And I had to know the ending . . .

*　　*　　*　　*

Back at the manor I hastened, almost rudely, up to the bedroom. As I pushed open the door I heard voices in the hall and then light footsteps coming up the stairs.

Swiftly I crossed the room and placed Grandfather's music box next to its twin. As I did so the end of the story was revealed to me.

It came just as I smelled the perfume, just as I felt the presence of someone behind me.

I turned slowly.

She stood in the doorway for a moment looking at me and frowning a little. Then she walked towards me. I pointed to the two music boxes. She stood there, gazing at them in mild astonishment while the light from the evening sun slanted down on her. And I heard again my grandfather's voice as he described his Elizabeth . . . Her hair was as fair as gossamer — her eyes were more blue than the summer sky, her cheeks were softer than a rose petal . . .

She turned at last, and smiled.

Even before she spoke I knew her name was Elizabeth. □

PASSING THROUGH

PASSING THROUGH

She had always known he'd be gone with the summer. What she hadn't known was that her heart would go with him . . .

Complete Story by
ISOBEL STEWART

L AST summer, I was in love with you. This summer, I feel many years older, many years wiser, and I know now just how foolish I was to love you.

I might as well love the wind, or the sea, or the geese flying south in autumn. Because they are free, and you have to be free, too.

You told me so, right at the beginning. You were always honest, and I am grateful for that.

"I'm only passing through, Beth," you said, that day when I'd brought tea and sandwiches for the men down to the field where you were all working.

You smiled, I remember, and your eyes shone brightly in the brown of your face. "But I'm grateful to your dad for giving me a job — I reckon a few weeks here could be very pleasant."

"Dad can always use an extra pair of hands around the farm at this time of year," I told you with truth.

It was what I'd said when I met you, that night when a group of us heard you singing at the hotel, in the smoky little bar.

I can't remember if the songs you sang had names, but I know that you sang about things that mattered to you, things that I realised, as you sang, mattered to me, too.

You sang about loneliness, and you sang about searching for peace, and you sang about the dreadful disregard the world has for the vanishing forests and the disappearing animals.

I spoke to you afterwards. There was so much I wanted to say, but I'm not good at talking to strangers, and that's what you were then. Then? Maybe you never were anything more than a stranger — a stranger I loved last summer.

And so I stood there looking up at you — I hadn't realised, as you sat on the stool with your guitar, that you were so tall — and all I could do was whisper, "Thank you."

You looked at me for a long time, and you knew, you told me later, all the things I wanted to say.

Smiling down at me, not saying anything, you put your arm round my shoulders, easily, lightly, and you led me outside with the dusk of the early summer evening, and we talked and talked of so many things . . .

We talked about the things you had sung about, and I forgot for once to be shy. You told me about your years at university, your few months of teaching, before you admitted to yourself that that wasn't the life you wanted.

You wanted to be free, to go where you pleased, to do what you wanted, with only your guitar and your rucksack for companions and possessions.

Wherever your steps took you, you said, you would find some work to do, something honest and worthwhile. It was then that I said my father could give you a job.

And so you came to the farm , and my father said you could use the room above the barn.

Every morning, through the long, golden summer, I woke with joy in my heart because you were so near, because this was another day when I would see you . . .

HOWEVER, my mother knew that you really meant it. She stood beside me one afternoon when I came back from the fields, and she watched me as I looked in the old mirror in the kitchen — the mirror that reflected the girl who had been with you only a few moments ago.

I saw her reflection behind mine in the mirror, and I saw her look at that girl with her soft, tumbled hair, her brown summer skin, and her eyes full of dreams.

"Beth," she said, worriedly, and I turned to her, loving her but impatient. Impatient to get back to my dreams — for you hadn't kissed me, not then, but I knew that you would soon.

"Beth," she said again, and her hands smoothed her apron. "Don't get too set on him, love.

"You know he doesn't mean to stay. Come the end of the summer, he'll be off, if not before."

I shook my head.

"Maybe he'll change — maybe he'll want to stay."

She looked wistfully at me, thoughtful, but saying nothing more.

I couldn't say it to her — I hardly dared even to think it, but as the summer days passed, the certainty grew in me that you would know, before the summer ended, that you didn't need to wander any longer.

Your restlessness would be gone, because we had found each other.

You hadn't even known what you were searching for, but you would know that you had found it here with me.

Before you ever kissed me, I knew that I loved you. And after you kissed me — that night when we walked down beside the river, a night, you said, that was meant for kissing — I was sure that all you needed was time, to be as certain as I was.

Afterwards, when my lips were still warm from your kiss and my heart was full to the brim with loving you, we sat listening to the river in the darkness, and talking.

And when we had finished talking, you kissed me again.

You knew then, I think, that no matter what you had asked me, I would have done it for you.

But soon you pushed me away from you, quite gently, and said it was time we were getting back.

My mother was working in the kitchen when we walked through the yard, and she called to us to come in.

She had just made coffee and when we were sitting at the white-scrubbed kitchen table, drinking mugs of coffee, she looked at you.

"Thanks for bringing Beth home, Rod," she said quietly.

You smiled, and I think, now, as I remember, that there was some sadness in your smile.

"It's a lovely evening, Mrs Carter," you said, "and the river is a fine place, but — I reckoned it was time I brought her home."

I wasn't a child! I was 19 — and in love, and my cheeks were warm, for I knew very well what my mother meant, and what you meant.

But I was foolish, for I read the wrong things into the steady, appraising glance that passed between you and my mother, and the certainty in my heart grew.

You worked hard, through the summer — in the fields, in the barn, around the house.

I worked, too, in the fields beside you when I could.

Often, as we worked side by side, you would smile, pausing for a moment as our eyes met, smiling in a shared, completely private moment, in spite of the other workers near us. I was totally captivated, whether you wanted me to be or not.

WE also went to dances in the village on Saturday nights. At first, you took your guitar with you, and when you were asked, you sang.

But when the heat of summer had begun to fade, you didn't take your guitar, and you didn't sing.

And sometimes, in these last weeks of summer, I would know that you were looking at me and I would turn to you, ready to smile. But then you weren't smiling. You were looking at me, steadily, thoughtfully. And once again, I read the wrong thing into this.

One day you came into the barn when I was milking old Bessie.

"You really are quite the farm girl, aren't you?" you said, sitting up on the side of Bessie's stall. "Do you really think you'll fit into an office, Beth?"

My heart turned over, as I thought what you might mean, and it wasn't easy to speak steadily.

"Of course I love the farm," I agreed, my hands moving rhythmically.

"But I've enjoyed the secretarial course I've done, and I'm quite looking forward to getting a job. Besides, I'll be able to help Dad with the farm books, now."

When we had discussed what I would do when I left school, my father and mother agreed with me that a secretarial course, and then a job in the nearby town, would probably suit me best.

I wasn't very ambitious, and it was all too likely that I would do as most of the farmers' daughters did — marry a farmer's son and settle down on another farm.

But that was before last summer, before I met you.

You sat there for a long time, I remember, watching me with Bessie, and then, abruptly, without saying anything, you jumped down and went out of the barn.

IT was a week after that, when the first hint of autumn coolness was in the air, that you told me you were leaving. For a moment, I couldn't say anything.

"I'm sorry, Beth," you said, quietly. "I did tell you I was only passing through. I . . . I didn't mean to stay as long as this."

"Why did you, then?" I whispered, my lips stiff.

You shook your head.

"You don't need to ask that — I stayed because of you, you know that. But I shouldn't have."

I wanted to hold my head up proudly and tell you to go. But I couldn't do that. I put my hand on your arm, and I looked up at you.

"The things you want to do, the places you want to see — we could go

Continued on page 19

GIDEON'S WAY

More impressions of life from the Highlands of Scotland, by Gideon Scott May, observer of people and nature alike . . .

Brush Strokes

While the curlews, who are the bearers of glad tidings, make a welcome return visit to the Strath, there's an uninvited guest in the shape of a "redcoat" named Basil, who's definitely not flavour of the month . . .

CURLEE, curlee, curlee." The curlews are calling again to tell all who are listening their name.

It is one of the sweetest sounds I have ever heard because it accurately forecasts summertime.

Curlews are the biggest of the seashore waders, with a speckled plumage of cream and brown, and they only fly inland when the Highlands are frost-free.

Then they can bury their long, five-inch bills in the colourful sphagnum moss and peaty bogs on the moor to get the sustenance that will take the place of their seashore diet.

They also change their tune to select a suitable mate and the courting calls contain excited trills and appeals to "Come to me".

This makes magic music for the hen birds and for anyone else who happens to hear.

IT'S lambing time once again and John, our neighbour to the east in Borenich Farm, must have forgotten what it's like to have a long, luxurious lie in bed, or even what his bed looks like, as he walks the hills, mile after caring mile, looking after his huge flock of blackface ewes.

He carries with him a medical supply to save a sickly lamb, and the expertise to save an expectant mother and make the birth of her twins a more pleasurable experience.

There are hazards, too — hooded crows which float effortlessly overhead like black shadows against the sun, waiting and watching for any sign of weakness in the little lambs.

But the lambs' greatest danger is a big russet-red fox that prowls the length and breadth of Borenich.

Unlike other foxes, he doesn't seek the cover of the woods and hedgerows, or slink around the side of the fields in the half darkness, but crosses boldly right through the middle of meadows in broad daylight.

I call him Basil, because he has a very distinctive brush. In fact, half of his tail is as white as the driven snow!

Basil knows all about the bright flashing lights in the lambing fields and the gas guns that fire threatening bangs every five minutes.

He has figured out, by careful watching and listening, that there's nothing to harm him here, so he treats these man-made devices that try to scare him with the utmost disdain.

I hastened to warn John about Basil, but he had more urgent matters on his mind and asked if I could give him a hand sorting out his sheep, explaining that his mother usually helped him.

The way he said it left me without the slightest doubt that it would be some sort of miracle if I managed to take her place!

JOHN has a lot of work on his hands running a big farm like Borenich single-handed, but he shakes off the weariness that sometimes besets his body with a shrug of his broad shoulders.

That's where his mum comes in. She loves to call at the farm and lend a helping hand.

On her first visit, I had a wee chat with her over the Borenich garden gate.

As we talked, John's mum told me she was more than surprised to see a big fox with a white brush walking at a slow pace through the middle of the biggest field, as bold as brass.

I knew this could only be Basil and when I got back home, I warned Irralee to keep a careful watch on her speckled hens, which went foraging to the far side of the hazel woods, because that is where Basil could be lying in wait.

Sure enough, the very next day Cain, our handsome cockerel, was having hysterics and Irralee raced out to find the fox picking up a mesmerised Maran pullet.

Irralee and the fox came face to face beneath a big blackthorn bush where Irralee took a deep breath and screamed her heart out!

This so shocked Basil, he immediately dropped his victim and disappeared.

The pullet, not much the worse for her ordeal, made her way unsteadily to the haven of the henhouse.

We haven't seen Basil since.

He just hasn't dared to come back, because apparently the one thing that really scared him stiff was a full-blooded female shriek!

STANDING at the top of Creag Mhor tonight, in the gloaming, what an indescribable pleasure it is to listen, once again, to the sweet, soulful calling of the curlews.

When the sun has set the sky blushing before it goes to bed, there's surely no sweeter music ever made to match this — it seems to reach way down inside and take my soul for a walk.

Highland legend has it that the curlews are the souls of people who just couldn't find the way to Heaven, and it seems to me that those lost souls have found a Heaven here on Earth. □

together, Rod," I said, not quite steadily.

I hadn't meant to say that. I had meant to remind you that there was a good High School near us, that a teacher like you would be welcomed there.

But I knew, looking at your brown eyes, already far away, that there was no use saying this.

Once again you shook your head, but this time with finality.

"No, Beth, it wouldn't work," you said sadly. "It would have to be all the way, the lot; marriage, a steady job, the end of . . ."

"The end of your freedom," I said, steadily now, saying the words for you. "But — Rod, if it had to be that way, wouldn't it be worth it?"

You were silent for a long time.

"I'm not sure," you said, honestly. "Sometimes I think it would, but — mostly, I think it wouldn't.

"I could be wrong, but it's better that I go."

"Rod, if you find you are wrong . . ." I stopped, but there was no room for pride. "Will you come back?"

You looked down at me for a long time.

"Don't count on it," you said, a little roughly. "I wouldn't want you to be hurt, Beth."

You went, then, without kissing me, without saying goodbye. I watched you walk up the farm road until my eyes ached with watching.

And then you were gone, and I realised that I was cold, for the sun had gone behind a cloud.

Yes, last summer I was in love with you.

But through the autumn and the winter and the spring I've come to see how foolish I was.

I've gone out, I've met other people, I've danced, I've been kissed. It's been fun, and I've been very happy to find that I've grown up, to find that last summer is over, and this summer I'm not in love with you . . .

But if I'm not in love with you, why are there tears running down my cheeks as I stand here at the end of the road, watching the dust as the bus drives off, watching, unbelieving, as you come towards me?

Your jeans are still frayed, your rucksack is shabbier than ever.

I see you through a blur of tears. Tears, because as you come towards me, I see the questioning on your face and in your eyes. You have come back as you wrote last week and said you would, but you haven't come back assuming anything, taking anything for granted.

You stop, and you look at me. I look back, and I know that the foolishness was not in loving you, but in thinking I could stop loving you. I loved you last summer, I love you this summer, and I will love you summer and winter for the rest of our lives.

I know that you have seen this in my face, for your eyes hold mine, searching, and then satisfied.

And we walk towards each other, slowly, until walking becomes impossible, and we run into each other's arms . . . □

19

AROUND THE WORLD IN 80 DAYS

Complete Story
By BARBARA
CHAMPION

AROUND THE WORLD IN 80 DAYS

— in fact, it didn't even take her that long to exhaust his entire stock of foreign travel brochures — and his patience! What on earth was she up to?

ALAN KENDALL wasn't sure he liked the new office of World Travel even if becoming its manager was a promotional appointment and they were a progressive firm.

There was something impersonal about the new premises, in a strange town. The vast amount of glass windows and plastic and aluminium fittings unsettled him for it was all so different from the snug village office he had been running a couple of months before.

Back home he'd known most of his clients nearly all his life and now he didn't know a soul.

Mrs Halliday, who did the typing and kept the place generally tidy, was a pleasant lady but very much engrossed in her family. She couldn't be expected to bother herself about Alan's trivial feelings of insecurity . . . besides, as manager he was supposed to be positive and dynamic.

Alan didn't feel very dynamic about his job, and his digs weren't very exciting either.

He had a small attic bed-sitter in a terraced house and the landlady insisted that the gas ring was only available for making tea and coffee.

"I like to cook for my boys," she said.

Alan was determined to find a little home for himself later in the year, when he was more in the mood, where he could cook for himself. It wasn't that he could boast about his cooking, just that anything had to be an improvement on his landlady's toad-in-the-hole which she served with disappointing regularity.

"I know you young men always like sausages," she'd say.

Alan did not like sausages and would have said so if he hadn't feared what the awful alternative might be.

AROUND THE WORLD IN 80 DAYS

If Alan wasn't sure whether or not he liked his job, the office, his digs or the food, he wasn't all that mad about the town either. In the main he was entirely out of tune with everything and he was unsettled and lonely.

Of course, all that would change in time and he realised that he would eventually settle down when things captured his attention.

Had he know that Belinda Clark would do just that at around a quarter to one on a dreary Tuesday afternoon, he might not have agreed to swapping lunch hours with Mrs Halliday.

STANDING only five feet three inches in dainty shoes, dressed in a flared navy-blue dress with cool white collar and cuffs and her curly hair bouncing about as she walked, Miss Belinda Clark swung through the doors of World Travel and stood before Alan Kendall.

"Good afternoon," she smiled. "You're new, aren't you? I thought I'd bring my business here."

"Good afternoon," Alan replied keenly. "That's very good of you."

"Yes, well, new businesses should be encouraged, shouldn't they?"

"Most certainly," Alan agreed. "And how can I help you, Madam?"

Belinda took a notebook and pen from her bag and then placed the bag on his desk near to a small wooden block which bore the words: ALAN KENDALL, MANAGER.

"Well now, Mr Kendall," she began, rather seriously. "What can you give me in the way of information on Maracaibo?"

"Maracaibo!" Alan exclaimed with open surprise.

"Maracaibo, Venezuela," Belinda said patiently.

Alan sprang to his feet, hovered for a moment and then sat down again.

"Well, to be quite truthful, I don't think we have much on Venezuela at the moment." He hesitated. "But I most certainly could find something for you within a day or two."

"They have a great bay of oilfields in the sea," Belinda said.

"Is that so? Yes, yes of course they have," Alan agreed. "And is that what you want to go and see?"

"Maybe, maybe," Belinda replied. "But meantime, what about Louisville, Kentucky?"

Alan was quick to indicate to this charming young woman that he was not completely ignorant when it came to world geography and general knowledge.

"The Blue Grass State and home of The Kentucky Derby," he said. "We do have a large brochure on the United States as a whole."

Reaching into a cupboard at his feet, he produced a brochure on America and handed it to her.

"You'll find Miami in there as well," he added, "and we are offering amazing bargain tours just now. It's terribly popular."

"Miami! Ah, no thank you, I've done the Everglades," Belinda stated.

Alan was impressed.

This lovely slip of a girl, so young, perhaps only 22, was intending to take her holidays in Venezuela or Kentucky and had already been to Florida. He wondered what her circumstances were and where else she had idled away her time.

"Could I have your name and address and I'll send you all we have on both places?" he offered.

"No need," said Belinda. "I'll be popping in from time to time."

She glanced around the office at the racks of colourful brochures and said, "Just in case . . . I don't suppose you'd have anything on Nova Scotia, would you?"

"Yes, yes," Alan hastily said as he opened the door of another cupboard and came up with a brochure on Canada.

"Here we are," he said. "I'd say Nova Scotia is much like Britain in climate and seasons."

"So I hear. Thank you very much, Mr Kendall. Can I take this?" she asked, indicating the brochure.

"Certainly, certainly, that's what it's for," Alan assured her. "I'd be delighted to arrange your holiday for you . . . I mean when you've decided."

Before she left, Belinda flashed Alan a glittering smile and said she would be in again sometime in the week.

THE office seemed larger and more cheerless when she had gone and Alan thought about the glow-haired girl most of the afternoon. He wondered if she was the spoiled daughter of a banker. He wondered if she spent much time travelling to unusual places. He had noted that she wore no engagement or wedding ring, and had felt strangely relieved about that.

It was Friday before he saw her again. Same time, same place.

Meanwhile, he had been unable to find anything on Venezuela but didn't need to tell her because, rather oddly, she didn't ask.

Instead, she said, "Good afternoon, Mr Kendall. Would you have any information on Marrakech?"

Alan Kendall was astounded and in his head he said: Good heavens! Marrakech! Why go there?

Out loud he said, "Certainly, Marrakech, Agadir, Casablanca, very romantic, Tangier . . ."

He handed her a vividly-coloured brochure from a rack on his desk. "Morocco is a fast-rising regular venue for holidays these days," he said.

"Splendid," Belinda enthused. "Just what I wanted."

"There are scheduled flights for Casablanca and several shipping lines stop there and at Tangier."

"Good, good," mumbled Belinda as she glanced through the various time-tables and papers he handed her in quick succession.

"And from Tangier you can take short boat trips to Gibraltar."

"Oh, no thank you," Belinda said hurriedly. "We did dear old Gib, six months ago."

Dear old Gib! Alan stared at this gorgeous customer and very much liked what he saw.

AROUND THE WORLD IN 80 DAYS

She was dressed in navy-blue again, her favourite colour no doubt, but this time her outfit was a smart skirt teamed with a pale-blue blouse. She reminded him a blue-eyed, slim-waisted doll.

One who was on familiar terms with Gibraltar.

Did she have an unlimited supply of money and time, he wondered. What kind of girl would take her holidays in such diverse places as North and South America, with North Africa as a possible third choice, a couple of times a year?

Tentatively he asked, "Is Nova Scotia out of the question now?"

Belinda didn't answer him — she wasn't listening.

"Have you any posters on Morocco?" she asked.

"There might be some in the back room," Alan said. "I could have a look on Monday."

"Oh, would you?" Belinda was pleased. "They evoke such atmosphere, don't they? The photography is always so good."

"I could send you all we have if you'd like to give me your name and address," Alan suggested.

"Good idea . . . Miss Clark. Belinda Clark," she said, then changed her mind. "Oh no, perhaps not. I'd rather call in because you have to fold them a lot to get them in the envelopes and sometimes the creases don't drop out."

The truth was — Alan would rather have her call in as well, and at least he knew her name now.

AROUND THE WORLD IN 80 DAYS

ALAN frittered away his weekend thinking about Miss Belinda Clark and picturing her in romantic settings on far-flung shores. By the time he returned to work on Monday he had decided she was a bored playgirl who travelled the world.

Or, more probably, she had a string of rich boyfriends who could jet her off to obscure locations at a whim . . . major cities having already been taken care of.

Even so, that didn't stop him digging out everything he had on Morocco, including posters, air and sea itineraries, time-tables, pamphlets on guided tours and an old calendar for November showing a girl riding a camel.

On Tuesday Belinda accepted all Alan's printed matter and then asked him if he had anything interesting on Iceland.

"Yes, we have plenty of interesting trips and package deals to Iceland," he told her. "But does that mean you are no longer interested in North Africa?"

"Probably not." Belinda was evasive. "It's a big project, you see, and I like to take my time over things."

"You can't decide?" Alan suggested.

"Yes, decisions are difficult," Belinda agreed.

Now, Alan was keen to improve business at World Travel and he was conscientious about presenting good figures to the Board of Directors, but he was entertaining a flickering idea that Miss Belinda Clark's business might not make a big impact on the company profits.

Over a period of six weeks she appeared twice a week, impeccably dressed and ever cheerful, and took away all the publicity he had on The Aleutian Islands, Trinidad, Madagascar, Java and Mauritania, not to mention everyday, run-of-the-mill little sun resorts and watering holes such as Guam, Spitsbergen and Senegal.

Alan Kendall, aged 26, smartly turned out, polite, calm and as reasonably pliable as a man in love can possibly be, adopted a sardonic attitude towards Miss Belinda Clark if only to defend himself from her demanding smile and her irritating inability to decide where she was next going to spend her holidays.

And there was another factor — sometimes she said, "We've done that," when he mentioned places she was no longer interested in. Obviously there must be someone else in her life — and Alan didn't like it.

Nevertheless, Belinda would regularly drop in at World Travel and persuade him to delve amongst his paperwork for details about crazy places.

There were times when he wondered when she would start on the other planets.

"Good afternoon and where have we decided not to go to today?" he would ask.

Or, "If you don't care for the scheduled routes to Labrador, have you thought about going by sleigh or roller-skate?" he would ask.

One day he said. "Have you overlooked the moon?"

Belinda always ignored his "funnies", as she called them, laughed loudly and seemed completely undisturbed by his sarcasm.

Alan did consider avoiding her, he did think about changing his lunch-hour with Mrs Halliday again — but he didn't think he could manage without Belinda's lovely face.

Other things had improved, though. Things had changed. Now he liked his job, he liked the office and the town and even his digs.

As an investment he had given his landlady a fine cookery book for her birthday, so the quality of the food had improved.

Furthermore, she was even chatting about converting the top of the house into a large flatlet.

"In case you ever want to get married and settle here for a while," she told him.

Alan Kendall thought he had found a wife, too . . . that is, if he could stop her globe-trotting, dispose of his rivals and bring himself to ask her out to dinner in the hope that she would answer a few preliminary questions.

Matters came to a head on the day he decided to be specially nice to her, but Belinda spoiled it all by trotting into the office and asking him for everything he had on Alaska.

"Alaska!" Alan shouted. "Why, my dear girl, who'd want to go to Alaska?"

Belinda fell silent and studied her pink nail polish.

"There's nothing in Alaska for the holidaymaker," he pleaded. "It's a military place, a weather station . . . submarines and helicopters drop in on Christmas Day, polar bears walk the streets and Eskimos have a hard time of it!" He paused and threw his arms in the air. "Oh, really!" he exclaimed.

Belinda smiled at him beguilingly and sighed.

"I'm sending thirty-seven genuine tourists to dear old Barcelona this afternoon and I can't even begin to contemplate imaginary trips to Alaska!" he shouted.

Without a word Belinda left.

THE following day, depressed and convinced he had lost Belinda for ever, Alan left Mrs Halliday in charge and went for a morning walk. He went through the park, alongside the new housing estate and round the back of the primary school.

The children were shrieking and running around the playground for their break-time, and he stood for a while watching them.

Suddenly a whistle blew, the children stopped in their tracks and then made their way towards their teacher.

Teacher was a neat figure in a navy-blue dress with white trimmings and her curly yellow hair shone in the sunlight.

"So!" Alan was triumphant. "Now I know," he said to himself.

Alan was delighted to discover that Miss Clark couldn't possibly be a jet-setter, a playgirl, a spoiled heiress or a world-weary traveller forever seeking new thrills. She was a primary school teacher with responsibilities and probably with very little spare time or money.

However, after his outburst over Alaska, Alan didn't think he'd have the opportunity of telling her just how delighted he was.

He was wrong, because Belinda came into the office the very next day.

"Ah! Miss Clark," he teased. "The schoolteacher in perpetual motion . . . and where shall we pretend to be going today? Now, let me see." He rustled the papers on his desk. "How about Borneo?"

Belinda smiled at him sweetly.

"I saw you," she said, "I saw you walking away from the school yesterday morning."

"You did?"

"I did, and I've come to invite you to Parents' Night on Friday."

"I'm not a parent."

"It doesn't matter," she assured him. "I want to show you something."

Alan regarded her with suspicion.

"Really," she persisted. "You'll like it. Come straight from work . . . you might be amused. Please come."

Nothing short of an earthquake would have prevented Alan from meeting Belinda at the primary school on Friday. When she guided him to her classroom he gasped in disbelief.

Entirely occupying one wall, under paper cut-out letters which read, A WORLD PROJECT, were his posters, brochures and maps all arranged in clusters according to the country concerned.

Taking it all in with the skilled eye of a professional travel expert, Alan was very appreciative.

"Good heavens! You haven't been to all these places at weekends, have you?" he joked.

"Truthfully, I haven't been further afield than Bognor Regis when I visited my Aunt Doris," Belinda confessed. "But for children this is basic geography and a simple study of the people of the world."

Alan smiled, grinned, laughed and leaned against the wall and roared until his sides ached.

"It's marvellous!" he spluttered. "Marvellous! I like it! But why didn't you tell me?"

Belinda lowered her eyes. "A girl doesn't give everything away," she said.

"Haven't you ever been abroad?" Alan asked.

"Never." Belinda smiled, her eyes twinkling with delight. "But one of the other teachers has asked me to go to the Isle of Wight with her this summer."

"Oh, don't go," he said. "I often get a few days off, with concessional travel, of course. Let me take you somewhere exotic."

"Well, perhaps when we know each other . . ."

"Yes, better, later on." He put his arm around her shoulders. "Perhaps we could go to Sarawak!"

"Or Singapore?"

They laughed and wandered down the corridor to join everyone else in the main hall.

"Or Samoa," he whispered.

"Or Suva," Belinda sighed. □

"COME HOME, ALL IS FORGIVEN"

Complete Story by
LINDA D. ACASTER

"COME HO[

That was the message he dearly wanted to give his wife. The trouble was, *she* hadn't forgiven *him*!

WHEN the tight spring on the letterbox clattered noisily, and the cat jumped on to my face with fright at the noise, I awoke with such a start that I was halfway across the bedroom floor before I realised it was Saturday. I wasn't late for work at all! I was supposed to be having a lie-in.

Through narrowed, sleep-laden eyes I focused on the alarm clock by

"COME HOME, ALL IS FORGIVEN"

ΛΕ, ALL IS FORGIVEN"

my pillow. The digital readout clicked silently on to 7.58.

I shuddered, more at the unearthly hour than at the goosepimples rising on my skin. Even the central heating wasn't due on until 8.

For a moment I considered returning to the warmth of the double bed, but I'd thrown the duvet in a heap in an effort to move quickly, and all the enveloping heat had probably escaped by now.

I licked my lips and reached for my robe instead. My tongue felt like damp sandpaper and my mouth had the after-taste of the cheese and pickles I'd eaten for supper.

Coffee would be my salvation, at least three cups of it! Then, perhaps, I might feel like managing a bowlful of cereal.

I padded across the soft green carpet of the hall and picked up the solitary letter which lay beside the door. Postmarked Newcastle-upon-Tyne, I recognised the handwriting at once.

Mother's fine sloping hand could not be mistaken and no-one else I knew addressed an envelope, "R. Groom, Esq."

Even after all these years away from it, her secretarial job at Powner & White was still firmly entrenched in her thinking. It would probably be signed, "Yours sincerely, lots of love . . ."

I smiled a little as I thought of it. Her and Dad's ways were so orderly and neat. It was a pity mine weren't the same.

I cast a tired eye over the kitchen as I reached it. Four days' washing up littered the draining board and empty food tins stood alongside the odd beer can, waiting to be taken down to the dustbin.

I chuckled ironically. Mother would have had a fit!

Plugging the kettle into the mains, I rinsed out the cleanest mug. The central heating boiler burst into life in the corner and although it wasn't throwing out any heat I felt warmer at the thought of the hot water pulsing through the radiators.

With my coffee mug steaming beside me I slit open Mother's envelope and started to read the two enclosed sheets.

She started normally enough; which plays she and Dad had been to see — Mother loved the theatre — how my Aunt Madge had sprained her ankle dancing on holiday, how there had been three burglaries in their road within a fortnight . . .

Then came the bombshell.

"We've been given tickets for a production in York. As it's on a Friday evening we thought we could make a weekend of it and travel down to

29

"COME HOME, ALL IS FORGIVEN"

London to visit you and Suzanne.

It's such a long time since we saw you both, we thought it would be an ideal opportunity.

We could get a train from York early on the Saturday morning and be in London before noon . . ."

The rest faded into a blur as panic swept through my fuzzy brain. I couldn't have Mum and Dad coming here. I'd have to put them off.

But as I thought back I realised how I had neglected them over the past few months, during the time when Sue and I were fighting to keep our marriage together, and failing miserably.

A couple of short letters, the odd telephone call, that was all I'd given them. I would have to see them soon, I knew that, but not here in London, not in our flat.

They expected everything to be fine between Sue and me. They expected her to welcome them. But Sue was no longer here, and I had never told them that she had left me.

And I could not tell them now, not yet anyway. I couldn't stand the questioning, the probing of how and why. I knew I'd have to see them but it couldn't be here.

I rubbed my tired eyes as I thought about it. The answer was simple, really. I'd meet them in York as I used to when I was at university.

York, the halfway house between Newcastle and London. It would be better on neutral ground. I could make some excuse for Sue's absence, tell them she had to work that weekend.

There would be plenty to do in York. We'd be so busy there wouldn't be time for any searching questions. It would be easier for me to keep up the pretence.

And why shouldn't I? My parents would only worry if they knew. Mother especially.

Was I sleeping? Was I getting enough to eat? She would fuss over her only son and I would probably get annoyed and say something I regretted.

Besides, it might be needless worry. Sue never actually said she was leaving me for good — a breathing space, she'd called it. She could walk back through our door any day and we could pick up the pieces and try again.

But I was kidding myself, living in false hope, just as I kidded myself when she told me she was leaving and I retorted that she must have been unfaithful — that there had to be another man.

Her reply to my accusation had been part incredulity and part contempt.

"What!" Her blue eyes had been as large as saucers. "Do you really think I would be stupid enough to leave one pair of dirty socks for another? You know, Richard, you're enough to put a woman off men for life!"

That had hurt. It still hurt as I remembered it, partly because I could see just how unfair I'd been. It wasn't the only argument we'd had which

"COME HOME, ALL IS FORGIVEN"

was turned against me. Sue was always so calm and clear-headed, I, on reflection, so unreasonable.

By the time she was packing to leave we'd reached an unspoken truce. I'd promised myself I wasn't going to say another word, but knowing that she was in our bedroom, filling our cases with all her personal belongings, was just too much for me to bear.

I lounged in the bedroom doorway, watching her intently, willing her to look in my direction, but she wasn't being drawn by my presence. Without purposefully meaning to I suddenly attacked her with sarcasm.

"Where are you going to, then? Back to Mother's?" I mocked.

Sue straightened up to her full height, quivering slightly as she tried to keep control of her temper — and her tears. She stared at me defiantly.

"Mother's?" She looked at me as if I was some insect which lived beneath a stone. "It's not me who needs my mother."

I still winced at that one, too. It had been a recurring theme in our arguments.

After three months of niggling ill-will, Sue had quietly broached the subject of a separation one evening when there wasn't much on the TV. My first reaction was to laugh.

"But who would wash my shirts and cook my meals?" I had asked, more out of shock than flippancy. To my astonishment Sue had exploded.

"That is typical!" she shouted. "I'm not a woman in my own right with my own career. I'm not even a wife. I'm just like a mother to an over-grown kid! You spend more time caring for the cat than you do for me."

Looking back on it now, that wasn't as silly as it sounded at the time. It even makes me cringe when I think how selfish I'd been, albeit without meaning to.

SO where did it all start going wrong? Mum and Dad had been very cool about our marriage in the first place. We were both in our final year at university and had been living in each other's pockets for the 18 months since we'd met.

"Don't you think it would be better to wait?" Mum had asked tentatively.

"Wait? For what? I love Sue."

"Yes," she said cautiously. "I realise that."

"Don't you like Sue?" I'd asked.

"Oh, yes, dear, Suzanne is a lovely girl, but you haven't known anyone else."

I held up my hands in amazement. "Mum, a university is full of people aged eighteen to twenty-one. Half of them are girls. Sue wasn't my first date, you know."

I thought that had closed the subject, but Dad cleared his throat and shuffled in his chair, ready to add his opinion. "You've moved straight from school here, to university in London. It's an enclosed community.

"You've not lived in the real world yet. You may feel differently about

31

each other when you do, when you see each other in a different light."

I hadn't replied. It sounded like a case of reverse snobbery to me, yet within three years that seemed to be what was happening.

I took my mug of coffee into the lounge and moved the week's newspapers from the sofa so I could sit with my feet up and re-read Mother's letter. The cat curled up on my knees.

. . . to visit you and Suzanne . . .

I should have told them about the separation. I should have told them about the arguments, I know. It was the logical thing to have done, but I'd tried to convince myself it would all pass over.

Even now, three weeks after Sue had left with her cases, I was still hoping fervently she might walk through the door.

But in my heart of hearts, I couldn't blame her if she didn't.

I hadn't even told my colleagues at the office. Nobody knew. They asked how Sue was and I said, "fine." Maybe it just hadn't sunk it, yet — or maybe I couldn't accept I'd failed . . .

But now Mum and Dad wanted to come down next weekend to visit us.

I sighed and lowered my head back on a cushion. I should ring them and explain. But no, I could just imagine the response.

Why? How? Why didn't you tell us before? We told you it would happen.

That was the one I really did not want to hear, the one I feared would be thrown at me. We told you so.

No, it would be better to keep them in the dark, for the time being, at least. I would give them a ring and arrange to meet them in York next Saturday.

I showered and shaved and got myself dressed. The phone glared at me every time I walked past it. I made some coffee, put puss out, had breakfast and made some more coffee.

By 11 a.m. even I had to admit that I was putting off this phone call. If I put it off much longer my parents would be standing on my doorstep asking where Suzanne was.

I SAT on the edge of the sofa, took a deep breath and dialled the number. Mother must have been sitting right next to the phone, for it was answered on its second ring.

"Hello, Mum. It's Richard."

"Hello, dear. How are you?"

"Oh, fine." I smiled. "How are you and Dad?" I was postponing the inevitable again. My hands were clammy and my heartbeat had risen. I was getting so worked up I totally missed Mum's reply.

"COME HOME, ALL IS FORGIVEN"

"I — I got your letter this morning. It was nice to be given those tickets for York."

Mother said something vague which I didn't catch. It wasn't like her to be so non-committal. I had expected her to enthuse over the gift and give me a bit more breathing space, but it wasn't to be. I launched myself into my rehearsed speech.

"About coming to London the Saturday . . ." The silence from the other end was overwhelming. It seemed to reach out and suffocate me. I could hear my own breathing down the line.

"Sue won't be here," I blurted out suddenly, hardly aware of what I was saying. "She's left me."

I expected some shocked exclamation, but the uninterrupted silence continued to hang between us. Somehow I was thankful.

"She left me three weeks ago," I said lamely, staring at my feet. "I would have told you earlier, but I thought we might have patched it up by now."

Still Mother said nothing. It was easier like this, getting it off my chest in one go.

"It's my own fault," I added quickly, "I took her for granted. She would come home half an hour before me and begin dinner, and then I'd get home, tired and irritable from all the travelling, and just sit and read the paper until my dinner was given to me.

"I never gave a thought to the fact that she'd had exactly the same hassle as I'd had."

It sounded a terrible indictment, even though I knew it was true.

"I helped with the washing up, of course," I added in my own defence, "and vacuumed occasionally and took the washing to the launderette . . ."

But everything was occasionally. For Sue it had been every single day. Keeping a home running efficiently was no hobby, as I had found out to my cost since she had left. How could I ever expect her to forgive me?

I looked around the living-room and felt ashamed at the chaos which stared back. Sue had rarely asked me to clear up, or do any of the other household chores. She had done them around me late at night while I watched television.

That had been the hub of our first arguments. A marriage was supposed to be a partnership. She felt she should never have had to ask me to help.

Suddenly I saw our marriage clearly, from her point of view, and what was more, Suzanne was right.

"Oh, Mum," I groaned. "I've been so selfish. I could have made life so much easier for her, for both of us, if I'd just done my share. How could I have been so stupid?"

"It's easily done, dear." Her soft words came as a surprise after the long silence. "At least you realise your mistake. So what are you going to do about it?"

Do? What was Mother talking about? Sue had left me. She had gone. It

"COME HOME, ALL IS FORGIVEN"

was her decision, but I knew I had to respect it. How could I ask her back?

Glancing around the room at the unvacuumed carpet and the empty crisp packets, I slowly realised what she meant, I could do something about it.

I sat back in my chair and crossed my legs. Perhaps there was still some hope.

"I'm going to have you and Dad down for the weekend and cook you a really good meal." Could I manage that, I wondered. Yes — Sue had taught herself to cook from books, and I could, too.

"I'll show you that I can look after myself," I said, "and then, and then I'll show Sue."

Yes, it was an excellent idea. I'd woo Sue back with a new me.

"I'm pleased you see it that way, Richard," Mother said, "but I think you had better concentrate on showing Suzanne first. Your father and I can come down any time. We'll forget about next weekend, and wait till you're both ready."

"But if you are coming as far as York next weekend, you may as well come down to London," I protested. "I know I've neglected you these past months and I do apologise." There was a pause at the other end of the phone. "Mum?"

"No, no, dear. It's all right. The travelling would probably have been too tiring, anyway. I don't think we'll bother this time."

Confused over this sudden about-turn, I said nothing for several moments — then something else struck me as odd.

"Mum?" I said. "You're taking this separation very calmly. Have you really got tickets for York? It all sounds rather fishy . . ."

The silence at the other end was broken only by a few non-committal grunts.

"Mum, you knew all along, didn't you? Sue's been in touch, hasn't she? Come on, Mum, tell the truth."

"Now Richard!" she exclaimed indignantly.

Suddenly I chuckled out loud. "OK, Mum, have it your own way. But I know you better than you think. Don't worry — your little plan's worked. I did need someone to bring me to my senses."

I thought I heard a sigh of relief at the other end, but I couldn't be sure. "Now, Richard, you know you shouldn't jump to conclusions," she said enigmatically. "Well, I should think you've got plenty to do, so I won't keep you any longer."

I glanced about the room and smiled to myself. "Yes," I murmured. "I have. Oh, Mum, did Sue leave a telephone number?" I'm sure I nearly caught her out there!

"Yes . . . I mean, no, dear, but I'm sure if you phone Suzanne's mum she'll be able to help you. 'Bye, now."

And as I put the phone down I knew I would be looking forward to making that particular phone call. It would be the beginning of a whole new marriage, one I would never let slip through my fingers again. □

"EVERYONE A WINNER"

Perhaps a fairground wasn't
the ideal place to mend a
broken heart — but it was
perfect for learning how to
try again . . .

Complete Story By
TERRI FELIX

THE excited, screaming children were barely audible above the
screeching sirens, the blaring horns and the impatiently clanging
bells. Rosslyn slammed her hands over her ears as the gaudily-
coloured fire engines, helicopters, motor bikes and double-decker buses
spun round and round.

"Come on, Mum!" Jackie laughed, squeezing her mother's arm. "We're

35

going home tomorrow, so let's enjoy our last night at the fair. It's maybe not the same as it used to be, but we can enjoy ourselves on our own."

They paused for a moment at a stall. A woman in a baggy cardigan was calling out numbers. Her fist was full of darts and a cigarette dangled from her mouth. Behind her was a panorama of playing cards perforated with holes.

Rosslyn listened and watched for a moment then took some money out of her purse and turned to her daughter.

"OK, Jackie, let's have a go . . ." Her voice tailed off as she saw her daughter's friend, Alice.

"Hello, Alice," she said, forcing a smile on to her drawn face.

"Mum, Alice wants me to go on the sky-wall ride with her. You don't mind, do you?"

Rosslyn's heart sank. She knew she had expected too much of her daughter, a bright young teenager, now steering a determined course towards a caring independence. She had no right to expect that she would want to wander round a fair with her mother.

"I'll wait for you here by the fence." Rosslyn looked at the tortuous machine which seemed to propel its occupants into outer space and then disgorge them looking shaken, disorientated and very green on the other side.

Rather the way she had felt when Joe had left her — completely devastated. They shouldn't have come back here again for their holidays but Joe had booked it when they left last year, as he always did — something to look forward to, he'd say — and Jackie had persuaded her not to cancel, said she'd be needing a break when August came round again.

Rosslyn had never really liked fairs, not as a participant, anyway. But it had been fun when they went as a family on the last night of their holidays each year.

She smiled as she remembered how Joe had always made it such a special evening, visiting every stall and having a cheery word with the stallholders. So much so, that it was like meeting old friends when they went the rounds.

Rosslyn recalled how Joe had taken Jackie for rides when she was a little girl, and how she had waited by the fence to hear their tales of thrills and bumps as they came away from the dodgems or the merry-go-rounds.

It was not so alarming when she was small. The roundabouts were safe and slow and nearer the ground. It was as she got older Jackie wanted speed, height and danger.

Rosslyn dared not watch as the monstrous wheel rotated faster and faster.

A fat man passed, hands in his pockets, calling his numerous children to heel while his pretty wife slid her arm through his and kissed him tenderly on the cheek.

A stream of young girls, twittering like starlings, eyed up a string of downy-chinned youths swaggering towards them like unruly puppies.

Rosslyn waited, alone. The wheel slowed down. A queue had formed for the next bunch of thrill seekers.

"That was great, Mum." Jackie's eyes were sparkling with excitement.

"It was really fabulous," Alice added breathlessly. "Let's go on the chair-o-planes now, Jackie."

"You stay there, Mum, I'll wave." Jackie and Alice ran off between the milling, happy, noisy people.

The noise was jangling; a cacophony of sound; blaring music, echoing amplifiers, shouting, screeching, laughing. To Rosslyn the sounds were incomprehensible, like an unknown language, blurred like unfocused lenses. She was no part of it.

No word was directed at her, no tinkle of laughter was tossed at her, no music charmed her.

Fighting back the tears, she remembered . . . The last time here' with Joe seemed a million years away. She felt the odd one out in a world of fun-loving couples.

The sight of Jackie's short, striped jacket amidst the mass of splintered lights and black silhouettes welcomed her back to reality.

Alice was pointing and waving towards a stall with teddy bears hanging from the roof. The two girls were making a detour.

Rosslyn smiled to show she understood.

She fingered the button in her pocket and resolved to sew it back on tomorrow. Her other fingers twisted a tissue into shreds. Rosslyn looked down at her boots — silvery grey. They matched her skirt quite well, she thought, and, at the rate she was going, would soon match her hair.

Recently she had found far too many silver hairs under the fading blonde for her liking.

With a sigh, she realised it would not be long before the special firework display was due to begin. She and Jackie could watch it together and then she could escape from this lonely place.

Perhaps the fireworks would relieve the tension — or would they just bring back memories she was unable to cope with yet? The fireworks had always been a magic finale to mark the end of a happy holiday. She wondered if Joe would be missing them. Would he even remember about them?

Her thoughts distant, Rosslyn watched the man opposite her rounding up custom for his goldfish stall. Naked bulbs glared at jam-jar glass; white, sharp, no frills. There was no colour except the minute flashes of gold as the fish spun round their plastic prisons dangling from the roof.

Rosslyn's smile faded. The memories were like a pain burning her skull. She looked at the goldfish man and wished she had never come. If only Jackie would hurry back so that they could move on to the firework display.

A laughing family passed between her and the goldfish man, handing around large dollops of pink, fluffy candyfloss. Rosslyn shuffled her feet,

"EVERYONE A WINNER"

the air was beginning to chill. She ran her hand through her hair. It had a dampness about it.

Jackie and Alice appeared at her side.

"Ah, there you are," Rosslyn said, forcing a smile. "It's nearly time we went over to the field to watch the fireworks."

"OK, Mum, in a minute, but we just want one last ride on the wheel. Watch us this time," Jackie called, running off.

Rosslyn stood still, watching them. The goldfish man glanced her way then turned back to his customers with a handful of white balls. He was a round, stubby man with a twinkle in his eye. His hands thrust continually in and out of the money pouch slung low under his bulging stomach, giving the money a reassuring jingle on the way past.

The white, bright stall blurred as Rosslyn thought of treasured moments, another self, another world: the world of before. The world of now was nebulous, a formless world without figures, without tomorrows.

The loud speaker system spluttered into life and a voice hesitantly announced that the firework display would be commencing in 10 minutes. Spectators were urged to take their places for a good view.

At last Jackie and Alice were on their way back.

"Had enough?" Rosslyn called as they got closer. She was cold now and anxious to get moving. "Can we go and watch the fireworks now?"

"Mum," Jackie said, her head tilted, smiling sweetly and not knowing quite how to put it. "Alice wants me to go to the disco with her. We just met June and Heather and they're going. You wouldn't mind too much if

we didn't watch the fireworks with you, would you?"

"No, of course not," Rosslyn replied too quickly, trying to cover her disappointment. "Be back before midnight though — have a good time and be good," she called after them, but they were already out of earshot.

Rosslyn was still mesmerised by the bright lights, wondering whether to go back to the hotel or brave it out at the fireworks on her own. She straightened up and looked across at the goldfish stall. Her frown was met by the old man's smile. He nodded to her to come over while he handed change to three giggling girls.

Curious, Rosslyn wandered over.

"Don't mind me," the man said, "but you don't look as though you're having too much fun tonight. Don't get me wrong, now," he said, lifting his finger to forestall any misunderstanding, "but I'm sure I've seen you here before. You come every year, don't you, with your man and the lassie. I don't forget faces," he added, seeing he was right.

"Fancy you remembering," Rosslyn said, surprised. She smiled as she recalled the sound of laughter. "I suppose we did make a bit of a song and dance about winning a goldfish."

"Not a bit of it. We had a good laugh. Besides, your man bought me a drink. Where's he tonight then?"

Rosslyn bit her lips, gesturing helplessly. Then she blurted out, "He's gone, just . . . gone." She turned away, struggling with tears.

The goldfish man watched as she walked off, unheeding while the first rocket rasped through the blackness showering the sky with mocking stars.

Rosslyn climbed the stairs to her room and sank on to her bed, dejected. She remembered the awful day Joe had told her about Susan. How could he have walked out on her after so many happy years to go and live with a young girl? It made no sense.

He had never come back, even though she'd heard they'd parted after only a few months. Was it shame, or indifference?

Rosslyn unbuttoned her jacket and began to prepare herself for bed.

JACKIE had already started her breakfast when Rosslyn came into the dining-room the next morning. "Hi, Mum!" Jackie called through a mouthful of toast and marmalade. Rosslyn smiled and sighed as she sat down beside her.

Their last morning — their very last. Rosslyn would not book another holiday here.

"Super time at the disco last night. You should have seen Alice, she danced like crazy and had everyone looking at her . . . Mum? Mum, you're not listening to me."

Rosslyn, napkin in hand, elbows on the table, was gazing at a distant scene played out the year before.

"What did you say, Jackie? Sorry, I was miles away."

"It doesn't matter, Mum. As soon as you've finished your breakfast, we're going for a walk. The train doesn't go until lunchtime so we're still on holiday till then, right?"

Jackie looked at her mother tenderly and wished she could have made things easier for her. Her eyes looked strained. She knew the ache her mother felt — the loneliness without Dad.

"Let's go down to the sea, it's such a golden morning," Rosslyn said as they set off. The air was balmy and marigolds glowed in the sun along the way. "We'll go through the fairground."

All was quiet at the fair save for an occasional bark of a dog or the yawn of a burly youth as the took the boards down from his stall and prepared for the day's work.

A lady wearing a hat and bedroom slippers hung a fresh supply of teddy bears around her stall. The goldfish man was sweeping up last night's discarded Coke cans and dropped toffee apples.

"Hello, love," he said in gentle greeting to Rosslyn. "Have a go? You're going to be lucky this morning. We've got to keep smiling, haven't we?"

"Yes, go on, Mum," Jackie urged, "you always wanted to dangle a goldfish on your knee all the way home."

Rosslyn lifted her eyes, smiling. The goldfish man winked at her and grinned as he handed her three white balls.

Rosslyn took aim and threw a ball. It bounced high, jumping over all the jam-jars and landing in the centre well beside the man.

She laughed. "I'm no good at it."

"Well, let me try then." Rosslyn was suddenly aware of someone standing close behind her — but it was the voice which made her freeze — a deep, dark, familiar voice that made her heart lurch and miss a beat and then race uncontrollably.

Without looking round she held out her hand with the two remaining balls.

Jackie watched, suddenly grave, as her father — the owner of the voice — threw the first ball. It missed. Even the goldfish man was silent and the smile had left his lips.

Joe threw again. The white ball danced over the glass jars, skated round a rim and came to rest on the bare boards.

"Oh, Dad!" Jackie laughed, breaking the tension. "You are hopeless!" She shook her head while her eyes smiled just for him then ran into his arms to hug him. "This is a big surprise for me and Mum. How did you get here?" she asked huskily. Her father hugged her silently.

Rosslyn looked at Joe, wanting to smile but confused, uncertain exactly how to behave.

Joe looked away, releasing Jackie. 'I'm sorry," he said, turning. "I've no right to intrude on your holiday. Couldn't even win you a goldfish . . ."

"Joe." Rosslyn called his name very softly.

"I'm sorry," he said again, turning away, his head down. "I guess I'll always be a failure. I must go now."

He began to walk away. Jackie made to follow him and all the while Rosslyn watched unbelievingly. She hesitated, then put a restraining arm on her daughter. "Wait, please let me say this . . ."

Then, running towards Joe she called after him. "We won once, Joe." He stopped and waited till she had come alongside. "Joe we can . . . we can always . . . try again." And she held out her hands to him and smiled.

Joe stood still, searching her face for an answer to his unspoken question, and then slowly, very slowly, he took her hands in his and the strain and tension left his face.

"I wanted to find you here," he said.

Jackie and the goldfish man watched them silently as they walked off towards the sea, hand in hand. □

LITTLE BILLY RUNAWAY

Complete Story by
E. JOHNSON

It was an unusual nickname for an unusual little boy — especially one whose dearest wish was to be "ordinary" ...

MARY RUSHFORD pushed the trowel into the dry earth, brushed a wisp of greying hair from her sticky brow, sat back on her heels, and listened.

A bee droned lazily by on its way to the apple blossom tree, where it alighted and began its work, unheeding of the woman kneeling on the grass just a few feet away.

LITTLE BILLY RUNAWAY

Mary shifted her weight forward again and withdrew the trowel from the crumbly soil. She stared at it briefly, shook her head, then returned to the task of weeding the flower bed.

You're hearing things, woman, she scolded herself. Advancing old age, perhaps? No, surely not that. Forty-four wasn't so old, was it?

With a practised eye, Mary sought out and removed anything that had no right to be growing in her flower border. She took great pride in her garden since the children had flown the nest, transferring all the care she had lavished on her brood of three to the upkeep of the lawns, the cosseting of roses and bedding plants.

"Nice morning, Mrs Rushford!"

Mary looked up to see George Shephard — the village postman — grinning at her over the fuchsia hedge. His normally pale face was red and blotched. Thin rivulets of perspiration trickled slowly down his plump cheeks.

"It is indeed, Mr Shephard," Mary replied, filled with compassion at the man's obvious discomfort. "A bit too warm for May, though."

"Ah, it is that." George Shephard wiped his forehead with the back of his free hand as he thrust a bundle of letters over the hedge.

"A fair amount of mail for you today."

The sight of the envelopes sent the familiar quiver of anticipation all through Mary.

Perhaps there would be a letter from one of her children. From Anthony in America or Susie at college. Even Michelle had been known to write once in a while.

She took the letters eagerly but checked herself at the sight of poor George's face.

"Come and have a cool drink under the veranda," she told him. "You're not in any rush, are you?"

The postman hesitated for a few seconds as Mary knew he would.

"Ah, well. If it's no trouble. I'm not too pushed for time," he said finally, ambling up to the front gate.

MARY climbed the few steps to the veranda and was about to open the door to the house when again, she caught a sound that was out of place.

She stiffened, straining her ears for a repeat, giving up when George appeared from around the corner, grunting and blowing.

Mary scanned the garden, wondering if anyone or anything could be hidden there. She dismissed the idea.

A more peaceful spot couldn't be found. The thought of an intruder was absurd, but even so, she was left with a slight sense of unease.

"Put your bag down, Mr Shephard," Mary said, grateful at that moment for the postman's company. "I'll just fetch you that drink."

George plopped himself into a cane chair facing the garden, a great gasp of relief escaping his lips.

LITTLE BILLY RUNAWAY

"My feet," he complained. "My poor arches!"

Mary smiled to herself as she busied herself in the kitchen. George's "poor arches" were a legend in the village. She re-emerged on to the veranda a few minutes later laden with a tray of home-made cakes and two tall glasses of fresh orange juice, the sides misty with crushed ice.

George's face lit up with a rare smile. He took a glass, a few cakes, then settled himself more comfortably in his chair.

This may be a long gossip, Mary thought. Though she would never encourage him in his gossip about the people of the village, she did like to hear the exciting pieces of news: weddings, babies . . . And the company was nice, too.

Although she was loth to admit it, she was becoming increasingly lonely without her children.

Yet, with an almost unbearable longing, she remembered the pile of letters lying on the kitchen table, as yet unopened.

As if he had been reading her thoughts all along, George said, "It must seem very quiet here now, Mrs Rushford. I mean, since your youngest went to college."

Startled, Mary managed to falter, "Why, yes . . . sometimes."

Sometimes? All of the time!

"It's a shame," George continued, "that your only grandchild's in America. No sign of another, I suppose?"

Mary smiled inwardly. She knew that George was fishing for some titbit of gossip that could be passed on further along. "No. Not yet, anyway."

Michelle's face — her middle child — appeared before her — sophisticated, very much the career woman. Mary doubted if there would be marriage, let alone a child, for a long time.

And Susie. Just 18, tentatively dipping her toe into the waters of life at her new college. Her eldest, Anthony, was well established, and married; a husband and father.

And three and a half thousand miles away!

George stood up, brushing crumbs from his tunic. He swung his bulky bag on to his shoulder.

"Must be off then," he said, touching his hair with his forefinger in mock salute — "Thanks for the drink and cake. Much appreciated."

MARY watched as he plodded out of sight around the corner of the house then gathered the glasses and plates hurriedly on to the tray. The letters were waiting for her.

With a clatter of glass and china, the tray was dumped on to the sink unit in the kitchen. Mary leafed quickly through the envelopes. Five: two bills, two circulars, one from a business colleague of her husband's.

She recognised nothing in her children's handwriting.

A tightness in her throat, Mary returned to the veranda and slumped into a chair. She gazed forlornly down the immaculate garden.

LITTLE BILLY RUNAWAY

You must make an effort to brighten up before Roger returns home, she urged herself.

If only she didn't feel so useless . . .

Stop it! Came the silent command. Your life isn't finished. You're only forty-four!

Mary knew that Roger was becoming concerned about her. Only that morning at breakfast she had caught him peering at her over his paper, his eyes betraying the anxiety he felt.

She couldn't explain why she appeared so riveted by a drop of marmalade that had escaped on to the tablecloth.

The sight of the marmalade had transported her back to the time Anthony had helped himself to a whole jar of it.

Just a toddler with a huge spoon, digging out the sticky, orange preserve until he was covered with it, he had thoroughly enjoyed himself.

But Roger had become so impatient with her lately. After she had found herself, yet again, recalling some incident long past he had interrupted her rather rudely.

"Stop living in the past, Mary!" His voice was edged with irritation. "There's a future for you as well. Why don't you try for a job? Find another interest outside the home?"

So she couldn't explain to him about the marmalade. She just sat transfixed, remembering to herself instead.

I married too young, Mary told herself. Had babies too young. They were my life; I loved being a mother and housewife but now I'm redundant.

This home that Roger and I built together has lost its spirit. It's a house again, a shell.

And what qualifications do I have to get a good job?

You're feeling sorry for yourself again, she rebuked, silently.

LITTLE BILLY RUNAWAY

MARY stood up, suddenly knocking her chair over backwards. That sound! A cough? Someone choking? She ran down the steps of the veranda towards the pond. There it was again!

It was louder now, more distinct. Sobbing — someone crying.

She found him behind the potting shed. A child of about six or seven, she guessed.

He was sitting, his back propped against one wall of the shed, knees drawn up, fists working at his eyes as the tears rolled down.

"My!" Mary blurted out, completely taken aback. "Whatever are you doing here?"

The boy looked up at her briefly with large, brown eyes then continued the sobbing and rubbing.

His light-brown hair clung damply to his forehead. His shirt was creased, his shorts muddy.

Mary dropped to her knees, her mother's instinct surfacing. "Come now," she said softly. "Tell me your name and why you're here."

He stared at her, the sobs gradually subsiding to silence.

"Billy."

"Billy what?" Mary pleaded.

"Billy. My name's Billy."

"You must have a surname." No answer.

"How did you come to be here?"

"I'm lost."

"Oh dear," Mary soothed him. "Then we'll just have to find you again, won't we?"

A faint giggle found its way from the boy's throat.

"I mean that I've lost my parents."

"Ah." Mary smiled, grasping a grubby hand and pulling him to his feet. "That's what I thought. Where did you lose them?"

The boy pointed vaguely to the back gate.

"Down there somewhere. The car broke down and my parents got out to look under the bonnet."

He paused. "Then I sneaked into a field after a mouse I saw. The car started up and when I got back they'd gone." He looked about to burst into tears again.

"Well, we'll go back to see if they've returned."

His mother must be frantic, Mary thought.

Leading him by the hand, Mary strolled along the lane to the road, a walk of about 50 yards. There was no sign of a car.

"I think the best thing to do," she smiled comfortingly at Billy, "is to ring the sergeant at the police station. They may have gone there when they couldn't find you."

Billy said nothing but followed her unquestioningly, his head turning this way and that as she led him towards the house.

"My garden is just like this," he remarked finally as they reached the veranda steps. "Except that the pond is a sandpit."

45

LITTLE BILLY RUNAWAY

"It used to be a sandpit," Mary said, "before . . ."

Those memories again!

She installed him at the kitchen table, a large glass of orange juice grasped tightly in his thin fingers.

The familiar tones of Sergeant Durnbridge answered the telephone. He was surprised to hear about Billy. He had had no enquiries about a small boy.

"I tell you what," he said eventually. "I'll ring up Bristol and enquire there. They should know if anyone does.

"Keep him there, will you, Mrs Rushford — until I sort something out?"

"Of course, Sergeant."

Mary replaced the telephone and crossed the kitchen to seat herself opposite Billy.

She observed him for a while in silence. He reminded her of Anthony at his age, although she fancied her son hadn't been quite so thin or pale.

"My mum's hair has shiny, white cotton bits like yours," Billy said suddenly.

Mary laughed. It was the first time she'd heard grey hair described quite like that. And he'd said it as though "shiny, white cotton bits" were a positive asset.

"Where do you live, Billy?" Mary asked.

"Bristol. In a house like this."

Mary went to the cake tin.

"Where in Bristol?"

"I forget."

Mary was perplexed. He didn't seem at all worried. Still, children had a knack sometimes of hiding their feelings.

THE next hour found Mary in the garage digging out her son's old bicycle. Rummaging through Roger's tool-box, she found a spanner and managed to adjust the saddle to Billy's height.

The time passed quickly as Mary watched the small boy careering around the garden with obvious enjoyment, the old, pleasant recollections wafting around her.

The loud thud of a car door slamming brought her sharply back to the present.

Hurrying into the front room, she saw a young woman dressed in a bright red top and tight jeans striding up the path. Her fair hair hung straight to her shoulders. Swinging jauntily from her shoulder was a brown leather bag.

Could this be Billy's mother? Not a silver thread in sight — and she didn't look very upset. Mary opened the door before the young woman reached it.

"Mrs Rushford?" A wide smile in greeting. "Sergeant Durnbridge told me you have our Billy here."

Mary felt a wave of relief. "You must be Billy's mother."

The young woman stared at her for a second then said slowly, "I'm afraid I'm not Billy's mother."

At the mystified look on Mary's face she went on, "Look, may I come in? There's a bit of explaining to do."

"Of course." Mary led the way through to the veranda.

Billy was still charging around on his bicycle to the peril of plants and shrubs alike, emitting loud whoops of delight as he did so.

"Let me introduce myself." The young woman dropped her bag on to the floor then sat down across the wicker table from Mary. "My name is Janice Davies. I'm a social worker."

"Social worker?"

"Yes — you see, Billy's done this before."

"Done what?"

"Run away."

Mary stared at her visitor. "Billy has run away from his parents before?"

There was a brief silence, then, "Billy has no parents."

"What! But he said —"

"I know," the young woman interrupted. "Which story did he tell you? The one about being kidnapped, or about the car breaking down, or . . . oh, his mind is very fertile.

"He's a problem is our Billy. We didn't think he'd go walkabout again. We honestly thought that this time he'd stay with his new foster parents."

Mary gazed down the garden at the young boy so engrossed in his play. "He told me he was lost. He was so upset at first."

"Yes, he usually is. And he does believe he's lost — or rather that he's lost his mother. He makes these trips looking for her."

"Why does he believe she's still alive?"

Janice Davies was silent for a moment.

"When I said that Billy has no parents it wasn't strictly true. At first, when he came into care, his mother visited him regularly. He was only a baby then.

"Afterwards, she stopped coming and she couldn't be traced. We never knew about his father."

"How awful for him." Mary felt a wave of pity.

LITTLE BILLY RUNAWAY

Janice Davies looked at Mary and gave a faint smile. "Not as awful as it seems. Billy has been accepted into several foster homes where he's been well liked. It's just Billy himself.

"He has this notion that when he sees his mother, he'll know her. He has a picture of her in his mind, even though he can't possibly remember her."

My mum has shiny, white cotton bits in her hair like you.

Mary felt a strange surge of excitement, remembering the boy's words.

"Of course, he pulls a lot of heart strings," the social worker went on, looking shrewdly at Mary. "He's older than he looks and very bright. He plans these little jaunts down to the last detail. Puts himself on a bus and goes searching."

A LOUD yell cut through the tide of emotion that was beginning to flow through Mary. Billy had fallen off the bicycle into the roses. "Billy!" Mary cried, fearful for the small boy.

They lifted him gently to his feet, delicately picking thorns and petals from his skin. Mary bathed the slight wounds with antiseptic and stuck a plaster over a small cut on his knee. She felt happier than she had for a long time.

Janice Davies led Billy down the front path. She turned at the front gate. "It was so very good of you to look after him. I suppose it's back to the residential home for our Billy now."

She looked down at him and ruffled his hair affectionately. "Until we find someone who fits his picture."

Mary was silent. She thought of Roger. What would he say if . . .?

Just as the car door was about to slam shut, Mary made her decision. She flung the gate open and grasped the handle.

"Would you please let me have the address of the Home?" she asked the young woman behind the wheel.

Billy, from the back seat, looked at her steadily.

"You're not thinking about fostering, are you?" the social worker said knowingly. "It can be a difficult job."

"It's a job I'm well qualified for," Mary answered confidently. "Very well qualified."

The social worker gave a short, happy laugh. "Then I wish you the best of luck." She scribbled in a notebook, ripped out the page and handed it to Mary.

As the car sped down the road, Mary stood watching, the scrap of paper clutched to her. Just before it turned the corner, Billy looked out of the back window giving a small wave of his hand.

Mary walked back up the path, around the back of the house. She picked up the rusty old bicycle and gently wheeled it back to the garage.

Of course, she thought, this will have to be seen to. And the pond drained and turned back into a sandpit . . . And, oh, there would be so many things to do . . . □

Sam The Seahorse

You'll love to sew our cute little seahorse

Materials Required – 40 cm, *½ yd*, of 140 cm, *54 inch*, wide fur fabric; 15 cm, *6 inch*, square of fur fabric in contrast; 30.5 cm, *12 inch*, square of felt for fins; oddments of felt for nostrils; one large pair of safety eyes; washable toy stuffing.

Measurements – Height, 30.5 centimetres, *12 inches approximately.*

N.B. – 6 mm, *¼ inch*, seams allowed throughout.

To scale up this pattern to actual size, squared dressmakers' pattern pattern with 5 x 5 cm, *2 x 2 inch*, squares is required. This can be bought from haberdashery departments or fabric shops. Each small square on the diagram represents 5 x 5 cm, *2 x 2 ins.*

On the dressmakers' pattern paper, mark a dot on each square at the point where it is crossed by a line on the diagram. Now join up the dots, taking care to follow all curves accurately. Pin all pattern pieces to wrong side of fur fabric, ensuring pile is smoothing towards the lower edge. Place pattern pieces with all arrows running in the same direction. Cut through backing of fur fabric only with sharp scissors.

Cut front in contrast, fins in felt and all other pieces in main colour.

TO MAKE UP

Gather straight edge of back fin and stitch to one side of body between positions marked. Slit positions for ear fins; gather fins to fit and insert, stitching

into openings carefully and ensuring there are no raw edges showing.

Pair body pieces, right sides together. Starting at large dot on nose, stitch round head seam, down back, tucking in back fin, and round tail to large dot, leaving an

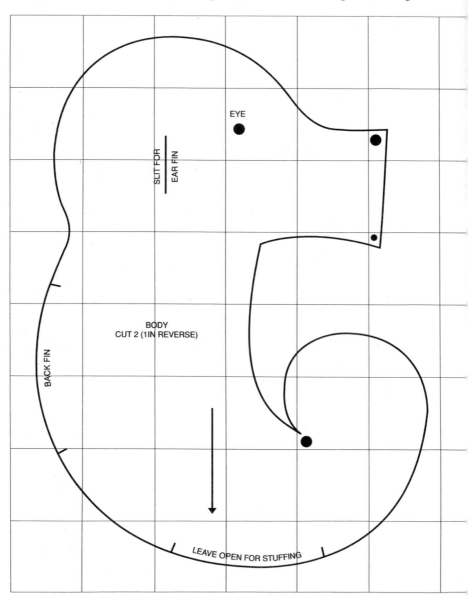

EYE

SLIT FOR
EAR FIN

BODY
CUT 2 (1IN REVERSE)

BACK FIN

LEAVE OPEN FOR STUFFING

opening for stuffing.

Stitch dart on front, then attach chin gusset above dart, as indicated. Stitch into position on body, matching dots. Starting at tip of nose (small dot), stitch to large dot on tail, then up other side, ending at tip of nose.

Cut nostrils from felt, stitch to position on nose, then stitch nose to body.

Turn to the right side, stuff firmly and close opening with slip-stitching. □

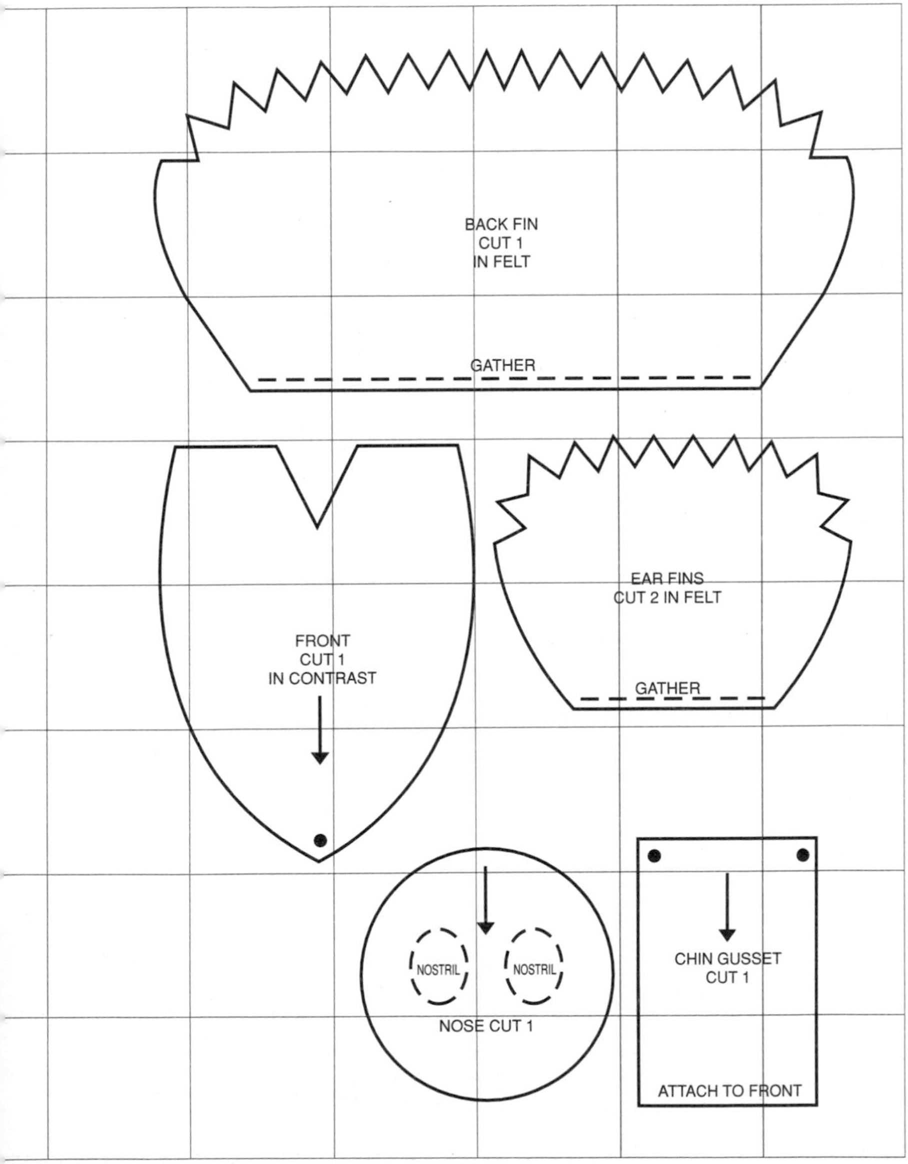

BACK FIN
CUT 1
IN FELT

GATHER

EAR FINS
CUT 2 IN FELT

GATHER

FRONT
CUT 1
IN CONTRAST

NOSTRIL   NOSTRIL

NOSE CUT 1

CHIN GUSSET
CUT 1

ATTACH TO FRONT

Complete Story by
SARAH
BURKHILL

"SHOW ME THE WAY"

He was so busy running from the past that it took a
very special person to make him stop long enough to
face the future . . .

IT was just starting to get dark when Ross turned off the motorway.
He eased his foot from the accelerator and dropped speed, mindful of
the changed road surface and of the twilight.

It was a dangerous time, night-fall in November, the time when so
many traffic accidents took place. He had been driving too fast. Stupid,
really, because he wasn't really going anywhere in particular.

He was driving from, not to. Driving away from the house he had
shared with Barbara for seven years, trying to put as much distance
between them as possible. Driving away from his marriage.

Not that he needed to drive very far to do that. The distance would be there if they were standing side by side, an unbridgeable gap yawning between them.

The journey was more relaxing now that he was off the motorway. It was the sort of countryside that was breathtaking in autumn when the moors were purple with heather, in contrast to the russety-gold of the trees. But now the trees were bare, dead looking.

Ross didn't like this time of year. He felt tired suddenly, and cold. There was a pub in the main street of the first village he came to and he stopped and went in and ordered a half pint of lager.

He didn't want it, really, but it was warm in the lounge, and brightly cheerful after the lonely gloom of the road. Half a dozen people, locals probably, were gathered at the bar, their eyes flicking briefly over the stranger in their midst.

Could they tell, Ross wondered. The old man in the corner nodded to him, then turned and said something to his neighbour.

Did he know? Was he saying: See that chap over there? His wife's got a lover. Been having an affair for weeks, and he didn't even guess!

It was the way she'd told him that Ross couldn't understand. The way she'd sprung it at him, suddenly, just after lunch that day. But then, Barbara had been snappy and irritable all weekend. Since Thursday, in fact, he remembered later. On Thursday night she had been very late getting home — so late even Ross had noticed and remarked on it. Since then she had been edgy.

He sipped his lager and tried to recall how the row that afternoon had started. The accounts, that was it. It was because of the accounts he'd brought home from the garage. Sunday afternoons were really the only time he could concentrate on them.

"Can't you leave it for once?" Barbara had snapped. "It's the first nice day we've had for months. We could drive over to Grangeleigh and see Aunt Cath."

"I want to get these finished," he'd said. "It shouldn't take too long. Why don't you go with Rhona? Take the car."

She stood looking at him for a long time before she said anything. "You wouldn't care, would you?" Her voice was quiet yet cold. "You wouldn't mind me going out on the one day of the week that we can be together. You don't care what I do. You never even notice.

"I've been seeing someone else — a man — for six weeks, and you never even noticed that, either!"

She laughed, and then she started to cry. And Ross just sat there with the accounts in front of him and stared at her disbelievingly . . .

"Do you know of a hotel round here where I could take a room for the night?" he asked the old man when he took his glass back to the bar.

A loud and good-humoured argument began over the respective merits of accommodation available, but the Salmon Leap Inn seemed to have most support.

"It's in the next village, going towards the coast — just down the

"SHOW ME THE WAY"

valley about a mile and a half," the old fellow said. "You'll be all right there, son. Nice and clean, and they won't rook you.

"Yes, you go to the Salmon Leap. Anna Elizabeth'll look after you."

He found it with no trouble. The inn was set back a little from the street, looking on to a narrow green. Ross sat outside in the car for a moment, wondering what Barbara was doing.

She liked to listen to music about this time on a Sunday evening. They used to do that together once, when they'd first been married.

Perhaps she was playing records now, sitting listening to the old songs that had meant so much to them.

Or perhaps she had gone out, leaving Rhona in the care of her grandmother.

Their daughter would be in bed by now. Had she understood any of the row they'd had? Probably not. It had all been quite civilised, not a voice raised.

"It's over now, anyway," Barbara had said dully. "I finished it on Thursday, because —" she hesitated "— because it was getting too serious. I was starting to care."

Ross blinked, wondered if it was really happening. They were like two actors in a television production. Real people didn't say things like this, he'd thought.

"At first it was just — fun, I suppose." She shrugged. "He noticed me, talked to me. And he listened to what I had to say. He was interested."

"And you weren't," she finished flatly.

"So it's my fault?" Ross had almost laughed. "OK. Fine. I see. You wander off with the first man who looks your way, and it's all my fault."

"I'm sorry! I know that doesn't sound enough, but I am sorry. Can you ever forgive me? I'm not saying it was your fault. I'm not saying it was anyone's fault. It just happened. And it's over."

She twisted the diamond engagement ring round on her finger and looked up at him.

"I loved you, Ross. I still do, I suppose. But I can't take things like they've been for the past while. I feel lonely and unloved and useless as a wife. I've had enough. We can't go on like this."

"That goes without saying," he'd snapped, and went upstairs to throw some clothes in a case . . .

"No problem," Alex Sinclair, licensee of the Salmon Leap, said. "We don't get many visitors at this time of year. How long will you be staying?"

A good question.

"I don't know, exactly," Ross answered. "Two or three nights, maybe. Can I have a meal just now?"

"Steak pie all right? Go through to the bar — in to your left, there." He pointed. "You can eat in about twenty minutes, and by the time you've finished, Anna Elizabeth'll have a room ready and aired."

Two or three days, he had told the landlord. What would he do after that? And what about the garage during these two or three days?

For once Ross didn't care about that. The boys could look after things, he supposed. He would phone them in the morning and tell them he wouldn't be in for a while.

They would cope — Eric and the apprentice, Gary, had been with him for over a year now, following the two years of struggle on his own when he'd started up at first, after being made redundant from Roundleigh Motors.

All his redundancy money and every penny of their savings had been sunk into that rundown little garage. What had Barbara expected him to do? Work regular nine-to-five hours and come home to her at night and forget it all?

No, that wasn't fair. She hadn't expected that. She'd been a real trouper in the early days. It was just over the last year that she had expected more.

Business had improved all at once, it seemed. He'd won servicing contracts for three local companies, and his regular trade was growing. He'd been able to take on two of a staff, plus a receptionist to answer the phone and help with invoicing.

His little business was doing well. And that was when things started to go wrong at home. Barbara wanted her husband back. She wanted more than a peck on the cheek in the morning and a tired silence when he came home late and went straight to bed.

He had become what they called a workaholic, Ross thought with a wry smile. Every moment spent away from the garage was a moment wasted.

Barbara was right. He was to blame but it didn't help, knowing that. It didn't make it any easier to forgive, or forget.

The steak pie was served with creamy mashed potatoes and sprouts and carrots. It was good, but he wasn't hungry any more.

"Nice dinner?" an old man at the bar asked him.

He might have been the same one as in the last place, Ross thought. Every country pub has its local worthy, always in his place in the corner.

"Very good, thanks," he said.

"Ay, she's a grand cook, is Anna Elizabeth," the old fellow answered.

That was three times he had heard the name, Ross realised.

"Who's Anna Elizabeth?" he asked Alex Sinclair as he showed him to his room.

"My daughter. She helps me run things here," the licensee said. "You'll see her in the morning. She'll be giving you your breakfast."

SHE didn't, though. Ross slept late when he finally did sleep, and it was Alex Sinclair who served him breakfast, hurriedly, before he started to get the bar ready for opening.

Ross ate quickly, anxious to get out of the way and not be a nuisance, then he wandered out of the back door, the only one open.

There was a small overflow car park on one side and a garden on the other, and he stopped for a moment, breathing in the clean sharp air of a frosty morning.

Continued on page 58 55

Give Us A Kiss!

Silly me, I didn't know,
About that pesky mistletoe,
Now that cat won't leave me be,
Until she's had a kiss from me.

Come on, I only want a peck,
No need to be a nervous wreck,
Now pucker up and go dog go,
We mustn't waste this mistletoe.

Oh dear, I'm in such a pickle,
I know those whiskers are going
to tickle,
Please go away, leave me in
peace,

Stop it now, desist and cease!
A little peck can't be that dire,
One little kiss is all I desire,
Come on pup, let's have a
smooch,
You're such a loveable little
pooch.

Hey puss, come back, please
don't go,
Don't waste this lovely mistletoe,
Another kiss would be just fine,
After all, it is Christmas time.

T. Ashby.

The Robin

When nights are long and skies are grey,
He brightens up the darkest day,
He's plucky, bright and cheerful, a welcome sight to see,
As he hops so joyfully from lawn to bush to tree,
And at our winter table, he's a bonny little guest,
Our winter friend the robin and his festive crimson breast.

T. Ashby.

A girl who could have been anything between 21 and 30 was pulling leeks from the vegetable patch. Anna Elizabeth?

She wore a calf-length blue skirt with a cream sweater tucked into it, and her hair was blonde and wavy, hanging to her shoulders.

Ross stared at her. It was her face that had most impact, and he couldn't think why. There was nothing very special about it.

Her skin was clear and healthy and didn't seem to be made up. A few freckles dotted her nose like a legacy from a long gone summer, and her eyes were large, although he couldn't see the colour of them from that distance.

Ross frowned slightly. She was devastating. Never in his life had he experienced such an instant attraction to anyone.

It reminded him of a picture he had seen in an art gallery when he was 18. A brilliant blue sky had hung over a barren, blackened landscape from which one rose grew, dead centre, a flaming, electrifying red opening in the sky.

Ross had been intrigued by the painting, had stood for over an hour just staring at the rose, fascinated by it. And yet he couldn't fathom the reason for its appeal.

The same fascination was there now, and he could have stood there staring for ages had not the girl looked up and smiled.

"Hello." She walked over, clutching her leeks. "You'll be Ross Boyd. I hope you like leek soup. That's what you're getting for dinner."

"I love it," Ross responded politely.

"I'm Anna Elizabeth Sinclair," she said. "You've caused quite a stir. We don't often get people this late in the season."

There was no question in her eyes, but Ross felt compelled to explain himself.

"I just — had to get away for a few days."

She nodded and sat down on the wrought-iron bench at the back door.

"Yes, most of us feel like that sometimes."

"You seem very well thought of in this area," he said. "I keep hearing about Anna Elizabeth.

"Why do they call you that?" he asked curiously. "It's like the American way of coupling two names, but in your case it sounds very — olde-worlde, not new-worlde!"

She smiled. Her eyes were brown, he noticed.

"My mother was called Anna," she said. "They tagged on my middle name to differentiate between us.

"She died when I was five, but the habit persisted."

She scraped a bit of earth from her fingernail. "In a way I was brought up by the village, everyone lent a hand with me after Mum went away. They do that round here. It's a very close community."

Ross wouldn't know about that. He lived in two communities. One he worked in, the other he slept in. There was no real sense of belonging in either . . .

"I suppose I'd better shift myself. I've a phone call to make," he said.

He felt reluctant to leave her.

"You should go down to the salmon leap while you're here. There's a beautiful waterfall. It's about half a mile away, going up past the church."

She gathered up her leeks. "It's the wrong time of year for the run. But it's worth a visit. I'll take you up this afternoon, if you like."

"Yes, I would like. Thanks," Ross said. He watched the girl walk away.

They met in the bar at closing time and set off up the one long street of Fitchdale. Anna Elizabeth had draped a shawl over her sweater.

She looked like something from another age, Ross thought, an age when elves and gnomes populated the valleys and witches lived in little crooked cottages on the edge of villages.

Perhaps she was a witch, he thought. Perhaps that was the reason for the strange attraction he felt towards her.

As if she'd read his mind, she smiled a Mona Lisa smile and began to point out things of interest on their way — plants, trees, birds that swooped and darted among the hedgerows, a common toad eyeing them balefully from a log.

He could imagine her gathering herbs and infusing magic potions. Eye of newt and something or other of toad. Or was it frog? He couldn't remember. He used to enjoy Shakespeare, but it was years since he had been to the theatre or read a play.

"I don't like this time of year," he said. "Everything dying as the autumn passes away."

"Dying? It's not really dying," she answered. "They're only resting, curling away from the coming winter. But in spring — in spring suddenly the grass and the trees will emerge with new life and the woods will be green again.

"It's a wonderful time of year. Everything is quiet in the knowledge that the time for new growth will come again. Don't you feel it, too?"

She looked at him questioningly. "Don't you feel this is a breathing space before you start living again?"

"It's a long time since I've felt like that," Ross admitted, and they walked on.

"My wife's been having an affair with another man," he said suddenly, after a moment.

It was the kind of confidence one sometimes shared with a stranger and then immediately regretted, but he felt no regret this time.

Anna Elizabeth didn't say anything, but her silence was sympathetic and encouraging and he went on.

"I think I could perhaps understand it if we were older, if our marriage had had time to — waste away. But we've only been together for seven years. We've got a little girl of four, Rhona."

He laughed. "The seven-year itch! I never thought about that before!"

"How did it happen?" Anna Elizabeth asked gently.

"It happened," he explained", "when Barbara decided to join a wine-making class over at Dolton.

"Good idea," he'd said vaguely when she suggested it. "I don't mind a

Continued on page 62 59

Rise and Shine

While a certain farmyard Romeo has nothing to crow about, Gideon settles down to enjoy yet another magical tale from Strathtummel's favourite story teller . . .

CAIN, our handsome pedigree Maram cockerel who has a harem of beautiful hens, is well used to being boss and ruling the roost, besides telling everyone and everything that "It's time to get up," just as soon as the dawn draws its first finely pencilled line of light across the sky.

It's in that moment that he stands straight up on tiptoe, throws back the scarlet comb that crowns his head and, with a resounding clap of his

GIDEON'S WAY

More impressions of life from the Highlands of Scotland, by Gideon Scott May, observer of people and nature alike . . .

strong speckled wings, crows loud and long.

But Cain has been silent for the best part of six weeks because he has been suffering

the misery of a moult with his fine, soft, gold-speckled feathers flying to the winds and the final humiliation — the loss of the long, sweeping sickle-like silver plumes that were part of the magnificent tail he wore with such pride.

But help is at hand. The particularly cold weather has caused a fast growth of his brand new feathers and, as far as I am concerned, he can't resume his crowing a day too soon as, with the exception of bats, mice and badgers, we have all been sleeping in!

STORYTELLING has always been traditional in the Highlands, especially during the long dark nights of winter.

Our youngest always begged for a story before going to sleep, so I would start with something like a little girl taking a walk in the woods to pick some wild flowers and whenever I paused to think desperately what I was going to say next, I got an attentive and encouraging "M-hm" which inspired me to continue with a description of the darkness coming down as she turned back with her bouquet, when suddenly a ghostly white figure flitted overhead and shrieked almost in her ear.

But it was only a friendly old barn owl who settled gently on the little girl's shoulder and, whispering softly in her ear, said he was just trying out his hunting call, that there was no need for alarm, and he would see her safely home.

Success, for me, meant the little one hadn't fallen asleep before I was finished and that the rest of the family who wished to hear the story, too, had crept upstairs one by one, to form a silent circle around the bed and give a chorus of contented sighs when it came to the happy ending.

THE best story teller I have ever known is Callum Og. He was christened with the name of his father with the affix Og which, in Gaelic, means young.

And now, when well past pension age, Callum has a round, beaming, cherubic face without even a tiny trace of a worried or careworn line.

Originally from Mull, he brought colour and character to Strathtummel with the host of stories he had to tell.

Tonight, he was telling about the time a lovely lassie had accepted his invitation for the last waltz at a dance in Mull. Callum couldn't believe his luck because traditionally, her consent was coupled with permission to escort her home.

In doing so, he put twenty miles between himself and his own house by the sea. But the soft, sweet, warm brush of Morag's lips, together with a tryst to meet again next Saturday night, made every footstep of the long way home worthwhile.

In no time at all, half of the journey was behind him, when he was suddenly aware that he was not alone.

Falling in beside him step for step, was a ghostly, gigantic figure in a long gown of luminous seaweed that shone in the darkness, like the dress of some sea ogre.

Callum was afraid but tried to still the beating of his heart by speaking a soft, friendly greeting in Gaelic, but there was no reply.

When they reached the crossroads the spectre took the high road and Callum took the low road.

"We parted," he said, "without saying a word, and I knew in that moment that the 'bogle' meant me no harm.

"Although," he added, "I could hardly keep my bonnet on because the hairs of my head were standing straight up on end!"

It was then that his wife, Morag, moved forward and giving him a fond kiss said, "Never mind about the bogle. I will always remember that last waltz."

CAIN, the cockerel, is clothed again, in a dazzling display of plumes that has the females of the flock swooning at his feet, and his incessant crowing in the morning means there's no more sleep for anyone within earshot.

But a glance to the east gives quick compensation.

The dark sky is divided by a band of bright ribbons, fiery red and blush pink, against a background of duck-egg blue, signalling the birth of an exciting new day. □

"SHOW ME THE WAY" *Continued from page 59*

drop of home-made plonk myself. And it'll give you something to do with your time."

Now, he shook his head. "How patronising that must have sounded," he told Anna Elizabeth. "As if somehow her time were less important or meaningful than mine. Just something to be filled.

"Anyway, she met some man there, and that was it."

He hadn't even noticed when she started coming home later and later from these Thursday sessions. Usually he was still at the garage, of course, and Barbara's mother was sitting with Rhona.

But would he have noticed, if he had been there? Would he have cared enough to pay any attention"

"Do you care now?" Anna Elizabeth asked, and she smiled sadly at him when he frowned.

"I don't mean do you care about the affair, about having been deceived. I mean do you care about your marriage and where it goes from here?"

He hadn't really thought about that, Ross realised. He had thought only of his hurt, the loss of that masculine pride which is so all-important. He had felt foolish.

"I don't know," he said abruptly.

He let his mind wander briefly to the early days of their marriage, but that brought a new kind of hurt, a different sense of loss. He shrugged the thoughts away.

He could hear the sound of water now. Not a roar, but a gentle rushing noise, the sort of noise it would be nice to fall asleep to.

"Look, there's the waterfall," she said. "There won't be any salmon at this time of year, though. They come from the middle of February on into March. And then absolutely nothing but death will stop them reaching their spawning grounds.

"When they get there, they just lie around in pools and rest until the autumn, when the females are ready to lay eggs."

"I didn't know salmon spawned in the autumn," he said. "I thought spring was supposed to be the time when most creatures' fancies turn to love."

"Ah, but the salmon are special," Anna Elizabeth said. "There's a legend about them in Fitchdale. They say the fish protect the village from harm, and that as long as they continue to come up the river, the valley will always flourish."

She laughed. "We don't have much to worry about. Salmon always come back to the river of their birth, though no-one knows for sure how they can tell which it is.

"There's something very clever and mysterious about the salmon. Another of our legends says that if you go up to the river at full moon and tell your troubles to the fish, they'll give you the answer to whatever problems you have.

"Or at least tell you where to find the answer."

Ross smiled.

62

"Do you do that?"

"I don't have any problems," she said simply. "I live in the most beautiful place in the world, and I'm surrounded by family and friends who love me." She shrugged. "What more can there be to life than that? I'm happy."

She was silent for a moment, staring at the sky, before she went on.

"I should have died two years ago. I was in a motor-cycle accident that by rights should have killed me.

"But it didn't and now every day is like extra time. It's precious, even the boring and mundane bits, because they might never have been."

Ross didn't say anything. He smiled gently at the girl, his white witch, suddenly understanding the source of her magic. It certainly wasn't beauty in the normal sense.

It was the aura about her, an aura of peace and wisdom and contentment. Almost as if she had found an eternal truth and was willing to share it with anyone who would listen.

"Thanks for taking me to the river," he said as they reached the side door.

"Thanks for your company. I must go in now. I've tonight's dinner to see to."

He wondered what she would say if he kissed her, but immediately the thought made him feel uncomfortable. It would be like scrawling graffiti over that painting of the sky and the rose, spoiling something that was a work of art, not a part of any world that would be real to him.

"There'll be a full moon tonight," Anna Elizabeth said. "And tomorrow we'll have rain, by the look of it, so make the most of your day."

*   *   *   *

She was right. It was raining in the morning when Ross left.

"My, you were late last night," Alex Sinclair remarked as he paid his bill. "Did you enjoy your walk?"

"Yes, thanks."

"I'm sorry you won't be staying on for a bit. Come back and see us in the summer. It gets pretty busy with tourists, but the countryside's a picture."

There were porcelain ornaments on the desk, little leaping salmon with a price sticker attached. Ross took one and handed over an extra note.

Was it for Barbara or himself, he wondered. He didn't know, really and it didn't matter. The ornament would sit on the mantelpiece. They would share it. They would share a lot of things, once the difficult time had passed.

Maybe one day he would even share the salmon legend with her, but not for a long time. He would feel silly, as silly as he had felt last night, under the full moon, talking to the fish.

He stopped at the telephone box up the road. When she answered, he told her he'd be home in three hours. □

Complete Story By
SARAH BURKHILL

BRIGHT LIGHTS

AND FARAWAY PLACES

*Once she had believed that she'd find her heart's
desire only in the big city — never realising that
dreams can come true anywhere . . .*

THE clock on Westleigh Church is chiming the quarter-hour, and I
turn over to glance at the small alarm clock by the side of my bed.
Ten to one, it says, but then I always set it a few minutes fast.
That's nearly two hours now since I came upstairs and here I am, no
nearer to sleep than I was then.

I tried all the usual things like making a cup of cocoa, and even
counting sheep, but none of them had any effect. So instead, I just lie
here, looking out at the lighted windows in the flats up on the hill.

I used to do that a lot when I was young and the flats were newly built.
Some nights I would lie in bed for ages, too excited by the beckoning
adult world to think of sleep, and wonder about the people behind those
curtains.

The occupants of the third-floor apartment to the right seemed to be
very late bedders. Sometimes it would be after two in the morning and the
light in their living-room window would still be shining.

Then there was the flat once down and across from them, which was
nearly always in darkness, whatever time I looked. Were they shift
workers, I would ask myself?

Occasionally in the early hours a bedroom window would suddenly
come alive, and I would wonder if someone was ill or if there was a baby
to be fed, or whether it was just another insomniac like myself.

What fantasies I used to weave about these unknown flat-dwellers!
And then, as always, when sleep wouldn't come, my thoughts would go
off at a tangent and I would wonder about myself, what the future would
hold for Claire Barnes, only daughter of George and Louise.

Where would she be in those misty years to come? What would she be
doing?

Lying looking out at these same lights?

How devastated my 16-year-old self would have been to know that!
How disbelieving, too, when all her energies and ambitions were
concentrated on getting away from little old Westleigh, that small
Northern town which seemed so dull and predictable.

"How could you bear to live here all your lives?" I would ask my
parents. "Nothing ever happens! Didn't you ever want to see some life?"

And my mother would smile absent-mindedly, and get on with making
jam for the church sale.

And I — well, I would get on with making plans for my escape. One day I'll get out of this miserable little backwater, I'd tell myself. One day I'll really live. One day . . .

And one day I did.

I was almost 19 when the job in our London office came up.

"London? What d'you want to go there for?" Mr Jones asked me incredulously. He was the manager of the local building society branch where I'd worked for two years. "It's all crowds and rush and noise!" He shook his head but reluctantly agreed to recommend me for a transfer.

"London!" my parents cried, mimicking Mr Jones' look of horror. But they too agreed that if it was what I really wanted, then I must go.

So go I did.

*   *   *   *

London. To me it seemed like the hub of the universe.

London! Tower Bridge and the Houses of Parliament. Fleet Street and Buckingham Palace. The River Thames, Hyde Park, Big Ben and Petticoat Lane. And soon there was more to London than any of these things — soon there was Andy.

I met him during my fourth week, at a toga party thrown by one of the girls in my new office.

"A toga party?" I asked doubtfully when Sheila invited me along.

She shrugged and made a face.

"Don't worry about it. You drape a sheet round yourself and try to look vaguely Roman. It's just a daft variation on the usual fancy-dress thing."

So there I was, standing in my improvised toga wondering what the people in Westleigh would make of it all, when a Roman god sporting a laurel wreath came up and offered me a grape.

"Hi, what's your name?" he drawled in an accent that certainly wasn't Italian.

"Claire," I told him, and he frowned.

"Claire? That won't do. You can be Septima," he said. "Or, no, Calpurnia! She was beyond reproach, wasn't she, and you're standing there like butter wouldn't melt in your mouth!"

I had to laugh.

"Come and I'll show you the mosaics," he suggested with a wink, and led me off to Sheila's hastily-decorated hallway. "Now," he propped me up against a wall, "tell me everything about yourself."

What was there to tell? My life had been empty compared with Andy's. So instead I just listened as he told me all about what he'd done in his twenty-two years.

He was an American, all the way from Arizona, and was halfway through a course at the London School of Economics.

His father owned a ranch, with an unimaginable number of acres. He had ridden bucking broncos, picked grapes in California, seen the Niagara Falls, shaken hands with Bing Crosby, and watched the sun rise over the Rocky Mountains.

And he was interested in me — little old Claire Barnes from little old Westleigh!

BRIGHT LIGHTS AND FARAWAY PLACES

LONDON changed for me after that night. My letters home were still filled with details of my work, the changes I'd made to my bedsit and the new places I'd seen, but these weren't the things that were important any more.

No, it was the little things which seemed too trivial to write about that came to matter most and to epitomise my life in the city.

Things like walking with Andy in Hyde Park on a summer morning, sitting on the grass under the trees, drinking tea from a Thermos and eating Chelsea buns which he'd bought because they sounded so English.

I remember one morning I made a daisy chain while we talked, and laughingly hung it round his neck. Hours later, as we walked along the Bayswater Road, he still wore it, looking like a descendent of the flower children who had blossomed not so many years before.

Another day, we went up the Thames to Richmond, and met up with a young crowd of his fellow countrymen wearing stars and stripes T-shirts.

We all came home together on the tube, Andy and the others singing "God Bless America" and me, not to be outdone, belting out "Rule Britannia" while an assortment of middle-aged Londoners looked on indulgently.

Oh, I felt so cosmopolitan, so young and alive and free.

Home seemed such a long way off then, more like a million miles than three hundred. Sometimes at night I would look up at the stars and think how strange it was that they were the same ones my parents and old friends in Westleigh were seeing.

But were they really? Everything looked different to me then, though perhaps they always do when you're in love.

I can't remember when I first realised that I had fallen in love.

Maybe it was the night he gave me the teddy bear, a big white one dressed in dungarees and sporting a natty bow-tie. "Dennis", he christened it, because he said it looked like a Dennis.

"What does a 'Dennis' look like, then?" I asked.

"They've got furry faces and wear dungarees," he said.

I sat with the teddy on my lap for a long time after Andy took me home. Then I took it to bed with me and cuddled it through the long night, as if through the bear I still had a link with Andy, still kept him near me.

I'd never felt like that before. Oh, there had been boys back in Westleigh, quite a lot of them. But not like this. Not like Andy.

Maybe that was when I knew I loved him. Or perhaps it was later, when summer had given way to autumn and the London trees turned russet and gold, and hot-chestnut sellers began to appear on street corners.

There is something about the autumn that draws people together, and as the long, light evenings darkened, I found myself clinging closer to my American, as my compatriots did to their firesides.

I was sorry to leave the summer behind, but the colder weather brought a new kind of enchantment with it — the enchantment of log fires in country pubs, of frost patterns on window panes, of watching haloed lights reflected in the Thames when we walked along the Embankment at night, arms tightly round each other to keep out the cold.

One night we met an old tramp down there, and I gave him all the change I had in my pocket.

"You're a nut," Andy said reprovingly. "He'll only spend it on wine."

But I didn't care. I was so happy and I felt I had so much that I wanted to give happiness, even of such a temporary kind, to someone else.

Suddenly I shivered, and Andy put his coat round me as we walked on.

"It'll snow soon," I said, and it did — huge white flakes that enveloped the city, softening the hard edges, blotting out all ugliness.

We made a snowman, Andy and I, and dressed it up in an old scarf and hat, and gave it bits of coal for eyes and a long carrot for a nose.

We went sledging, and visited the park to see the bare branches of trees etched white against the sky, like in the Christmas card Mum and Dad had sent me.

I'd gone home at Christmas, but only for three days, unable to stand the thought of being away from him for any longer.

"You should have brought your friend back with you," Mum said, but something had told me that would have been a mistake. Andy in Westleigh, coming to the watchnight service with us, and passing turkey sandwiches to old Mrs Lawson who always came in on Christmas night?

No, it was unimaginable!

AND so life went on, and the season changed again. Suddenly winter had gone and we were into spring. The displays in the parks changed to daffodils and tulips and beds of blue and white hyacinths in the shape of clocks.

But as the spring flowers bloomed, there was a new chill in my heart. Soon Andy would be going away, his course would be over, and he would return to America.

"Come with me," he said cheerfully. "There's nothing to keep you here, is there?"

What did he mean, exactly, I wondered. Was he talking about marriage, or what?

It didn't matter anyway, for all of a sudden there was no time to think of Andy and what the future might hold. Suddenly, with that devastating phone call from Westleigh, all that mattered was the present.

Mum didn't break the news to me gently, she was too upset herself for the niceties of these things.

"Dad's had a stroke. Come home at once."

So I went home, of course. Home to Westleigh. Home to see the first man I had ever loved lying in a hospital bed, unable to move, unable to speak. And my mother and I clung together in our bewilderment and unhappiness.

"What's going to happen?" I asked our doctor quietly. I couldn't bring myself to ask the questions which were constantly going through my brain. Is he going to die? Will he ever see me, touch me, speak to me again? Will I ever be able to forgive myself for not being here?

How can you ask such questions of a stranger? Perhaps if it had been old Dr Arthur, that all-knowing sage of my childhood, I might have done. But this was a new man, a stranger, proof that in my absence things in Westleigh had not stood still.

Perhaps, though, he read all these things into my question, for Dr Scott looked at me with something more than a doctor's professional, practised compassion.

"I don't know," he said honestly. "But I've come to know your father quite well in the few months I've been here, and I know that if willpower has anything to do with it, he should come through. We can only hope."

He looked away. "And we can pray, too."

Were these prayers working, I wondered a few weeks later. Dad's speech was returning a little — slowly, oh so slowly. Gradually movement was coming back to his arms, and he was able to reach out his hand to take the flowers I brought up from the garden.

He certainly seemed to be getting better, so much so that, guiltily, I found my thoughts returning to London, and to Andy.

"Why don't you go down for the weekend?" my mother asked, as if she'd been reading my thoughts. "You'll have to see the landlord about your bedsit. Whether you're keeping it on or giving it up," she added with forced casualness, "you'll have lots to arrange and it's easier if you're on the spot."

London. How different it looked from the last time I arrived, and yet it wasn't really any different at all.

"How's your old man?"

BRIGHT LIGHTS FARAWAY PLACES

Andy asked. He was packing books into a trunk, his flat a chaotic mess with all the last-minute clearing up.

"Getting better, I think," I told him.

"Great!" He examined a title, then threw it on to a pile to be discarded. "Maybe you'll be able to get over to the States for a holiday some time later this year, then."

I looked at him warily, feeling strange and uncomfortable amongst all this activity.

"Would you like me to?" I asked.

"Sure I would." Andy stopped for a moment, and ruffled my hair. "You made London good for me, Claire. Really special. I'd enjoy showing you something of my country. I owe you, don't I?"

He owed me? But it shouldn't be like that, I wanted to shout at him. I shouldn't be a debt to be repaid, hospitality returned and all things equal.

"It'll be good to get back again," he went on. "Corny though it may sound, there's no place like home, is there?"

I watched sadly as he continued his packing. You're home already, I thought, miles away from me. You've become a stranger in these few, short weeks.

But perhaps he would have been a stranger anyway, away from the environment in which I knew him. London had been a time out of his life. Now he was going home to his real world, as I must go home to mine.

For it was my real world. I knew that as Westleigh enfolded me in its arms, just as it does any of its sons and daughters who are facing difficulty.

The whole town seemed to rally round when my father came home from hospital. Mrs Lawson came over with gallons of her home-made tonic wine. George Adams dug over the garden for us, and filled it with summer bedding plants he'd been bringing on from seed.

The Thompsons offered the use of their car any time we needed it and Mr Jones moved heaven and earth to get me my old job back.

Gradually my father did get better. Not well, of course. He would never be that. He would always walk with a stick. He couldn't be expected to work again.

But he had come through it, and slowly life settled into a new pattern for him, and for me, too.

Things changed in Westleigh over the next few years. More flats were built at Dyke Head. Dr Scott gave up general practice to do research work.

Part of the church tower collapsed, and a massive fund-raising campaign took place to restore it.

But some things never change — like the spirit that makes a community. The generosity and goodness and day-to-day fortitude of its people. The sense of belonging that one finds in such a community.

How could I ever have hated you, I wondered. How could I ever have thought you small-minded and prying and provincial!

London and Andy seemed such a long time ago then, although it could only have been seven years or so.

I thought about him sometimes, of course. I thought about how different everything might have been. But not very often. For one thing, I was too busy making myself a part of that community I had ignored for years. And for another, well, things look different in retrospect. Would they have worked out the way I imagined at 19? Probably not. They seldom do, in real life.

The clock on St Mary's impressive renovated tower is striking again. Goodness, I must get some sleep. Tomorrow I'll be a wreck, when I should be looking my best.

A light has come on in the second-floor flat, the one to the left. What's going on behind that curtained window, I wonder.

Is Jack up making a cup of tea, perhaps rehearsing his speech for tomorrow? Or maybe he's just checking that the ring is still safe in the top drawer of the bureau.

He's a careful, methodical man, Jack Scott. I knew that from the first week I met him, when he was tending Dad with such loving care, and the impression was reinforced later when we both helped with the church tower appeal.

He will have everything checked and double checked, so that tomorrow's celebrations go as beautifully as we've planned.

There is a movement in the hallway, a slow measured tread that tells me it is my father.

"Dad?" I call out. "What's wrong? Can't you sleep?"

He comes into my room, eases himself down on the edge of the bed.

"Don't you worry, lass, I'm just going to get a cup of tea. I keep thinking about tomorrow, hoping I'll manage all right."

I know he's frowning. I can see the lowering of his brow in the darkness.

"You should have got your Uncle Ted to do this, you know," he says quietly. "I'll only keep everybody back, trying to get up the aisle with this leg of mine."

"Rubbish! Who could possibly give me away but you?" I reach over to kiss his cheek. "Anyway, you'll manage fine. Jack said so, and he should know."

"Ay, well, maybe." He smiles. "But you get to sleep now, or you'll not be managing so fine yourself!"

The light in Jack's window has gone out as I settle myself back on to the pillows and I hope that he too will find sleep easier now.

Life is a funny old thing, isn't it? If all my youthful dreams had come true, if everything had gone as I wished it, then this morning I wouldn't be on the verge of marrying the most wonderful man in the whole wide world.

Where would I be, I wonder.

But it doesn't really matter. There is no place on earth I would rather be, no-one I would rather be with — for now, and for always. □

THE HAPPINESS MAN

Complete Story by
ELIZABETH
ASHCROFT

**Outraged, she watched as, one
by one, her neighbours fell under the spell of —**

THE
HAPPINESS MAN

AMELIA JEVONS leaned on the balcony of her small flat and peered crossly down at the communal gardens. He'd done it again. Right next to her own jumpers and underwear, that Mr Price had his garish, crumpled, striped pyjamas. And a sweater with holes in the sleeves blew happily entangled with her blue nightdress. It was bad enough having to share a communal washing line, but to have to share with Mr Price, of all people!

She remembered the first time she'd found out he was her new

72

neighbour, on a bright spring day with clouds scudding across the sky.

She'd gone upstairs clutching a box of petunias, a bag of compost, and downstairs had come a chunky blue-eyed man carrying a hoe. He'd crashed right into her without so much as an apology. The bag of compost, of course, had burst. The stranger had gazed at the petunias in her hand.

"Another gardener! Well that's good news. Putting them in pots, are you, on the balcony?"

She nodded speechlessly. The hoe was dangerously near her left eye, and in the other hand the man carried a pair of very sharp shears.

"What are you doing?" she asked.

The third form at the school where she had taught for so long had always gone very quiet when she used that tone. This stranger just beamed at her.

"Going to take up all those weeds along the fence. I can't think what the janitor chap is playing at. Then I'm going to plant some flowers. Petunias, maybe!" he said jovially, darting a bright-eyed glance at her. "Lovely splash of colour they always make."

Miss Jevons took a deep breath. She'd seen the men move this man in, only five days ago, and already he was trying to take over Potter's job.

"Mr Potter is a janitor," she said, "not the gardener. He does odd jobs, admittedly, but there is a garden service which comes round regularly. And," she added with dignity, "you are likely to start Mr Potter complaining. I think I saw you putting up a trellis on your balcony this morning. We are not supposed to put things on balconies."

"Oh, bosh," he said. "Rules are made to be broken. I'll do what I like on my own terrace."

Miss Jevons stiffened. Rules were made to be kept, they made life orderly, neat, uncomplicated. She'd never, to her knowledge, broken a rule.

"I'll put one up for you if you like," he offered surprisingly. "I'm going to grow sweet peas and hang nuts for the birds. Encourage wild life, conserve nature, that's my motto." And with that, he disappeared down the concrete stairs.

Then the next day he hung out his washing.

Mrs Sweet, who'd had the flat before, had an unwritten agreement with Miss Jevons. On Mondays, Wednesdays and Fridays, she hung her washing on the bright yellow whirligig — on Tuesdays, Thursdays and Saturdays, Miss Jevons used it. And the arrangement had worked very well.

But Mr Price appeared on Tuesday morning as she was pegging out her washing on a breezy day, and proceeded to hang up his own rather grey underwear next to hers and even helped himself to one of the pegs from her pegbag hanging on the line.

"Mr Price! Those are my pegs!"

"Uh? Oh, sorry," he said absently, taking another.

THE HAPPINESS MAN

"Lovely day for washing, isn't it, Miss Jevons? May I say, you get yours lovely and clean." He glanced admiringly at her best yellow slip with the lace, and she flushed.

"Mr Price. This is not your day, and I should be glad if you would take your washing down. Tomorrow is your day."

"My day? What do you mean? I can use the line whenever I want. You won't mind if I share a line with you, will you?"

She went pink with indignation. "I do mind. Mrs Sweet and I always used alternate days." She looked at him over a billowing pink nylon sheet, and he went on calmly hanging out baggy sweaters and dingy tea-towels. "Especially," she added, "as your washing isn't even very clean."

He grunted, busily struggling with a tablecloth which suddenly blew over Miss Jevons' head, enveloping her in red check seersucker and what looked suspiciously like tomato sauce stains.

"Clean enough," he said. "Machine's broken, so I'm doing it by hand. Shan't bother to get it repaired," he added cheerfully. "Got better things to do."

"Such as?" she asked coldly, and he grinned. He seemed, she thought bitterly, utterly unquellable. For the very first time she began to regret taking one of the flats when she'd retired a year ago.

"Fishing, gardening, sitting in the sun, reading, listening to Beethoven. What do you do in your spare time? When you're not doing your washing?"

"I — really, Mr Price! It is no concern of yours what I do in my spare time. Not that I have much time to spare," she added, thinking of the old people's club where she helped, and her shining, spick and span flat. And the books she read for one hour every evening when she'd switched the TV off after the ten o'clock news.

That reminded her. "Mr Price, could you possibly turn your TV set down at night? It's right next to my bedroom. It is very loud."

He looked surprised. "Go to bed early, do you?"

"No," she said. "I just like to read, quietly, for an hour every evening. And I cannot, with your cowboys and TV detectives clattering away next door."

He was clearly interested. "Hear it through the walls, do you? Foreign built. Well, I'm off fishing. You ought to enjoy yourself a bit more, Miss Jevons. Get some fun out of life."

With that he clumped upstairs, leaving his disreputable washing swinging round on the line. She watched it, frowning. She would have a word with the janitor. Maybe he could help her.

BUT Mr Potter couldn't. Nowhere in the contract was there anything about using the line on alternate days. "Afraid you'll just have to put up with it, Miss Jevons," he said gloomily. "But I'm not putting up with the way he's chopped down my hedge, and dug up all the weeds, too."

That was the week Mr Potter went on strike. The other residents gathered indignantly in their communal halls or by their communal washing lines.

"Mr Potter hasn't even taken out the dustbins to be emptied. Or cleaned up our hall. Or swept the paths. Look at them, all covered in leaves!"

Mr Price came downstairs, with his fishing rod over one shoulder, whistling loudly and untunefully.

"What's all this? Action committee? Protest meeting? Where are the banners?"

"It is," Miss Jevons said succinctly, "a protest meeting."

He grinned. "All for a bit of protesting myself. What are you protesting about? I'll give you a hand."

"Hardly," she returned, drily. "It's your fault we're protesting. Mr Potter's gone on strike."

"Potter? Whatever for?"

"Because you've interfered with his job, cutting his hedges down and digging up his weeds."

He looked astonished."

"Rubbish! Only helped the man. Should have thought he'd be pleased — give him more time to do his sweeping and his dustbins. Can't stop. Got an appointment with a fish."

And now here he was with his washing on the line again, and a few minutes ago a notice had been posted in the communal lounge.

We regret that the gardening service will not be round this week to cut the lawn. They are taking action over one of the residents cutting the lawn under his window. Will residents please take note, if they wish the grounds to continue to be pleasant and tidy.

"Tidy!" Mr Price exploded later. "Too tidy, they are."

Miss Jevons had just seen him peering at the notice-board, his face red from an afternoon's fishing, and he smelled strongly of tobacco and fish. She backed away, wrinkling her nose.

"And what is your idea of a garden, Mr Price? You were the one who started this, chopping down the weeds."

"A homely garden," he said. "Lived in, not formal. Bulbs and flowers growing under the trees, in the grass. Not concrete with squares of earth and one miserable scraggy rose sticking in it. Long grass, with daisies." For a moment he sounded vulnerable, almost wistful.

"There's nothing to beat the smell of grass, and the look of daisies, white and nodding and pretty in the summer sun. Reminds me of daisy chains, and when I was young."

He stared through the window at the squares of grass and squares of concrete with washing lines neatly embedded, equi-distant to each other, all the same height and same colour. Suddenly Miss Jevons was swept back into her own childhood . . .

The untidy vicarage garden, with clumps of lupins leaning

companionably against each other, huge flag iris, taller than she was. The humming of bees and the long, cool, grass which tickled her legs when she sat in it, picking daisies, and bright yellow buttercups to make necklaces.

Then she shook herself. That was a long time ago. And how did Mr Price think that they could have an informal garden in a place like this, anyway? The way things were going, they would certainly have plenty of daisies and grass, if the contractors didn't come to mow the lawns.

"And I suppose," she said sternly, "if the contractors don't come any more, you'll be good enough to cut the grass for us, Mr Price? And you could plant bulbs under the washing lines, just to add a touch of informality."

Impervious as always to her insults, he grinned. "Now Miss Jevons, what a good idea. Crocuses, I think. Bright yellow to cheer us all up. And a pond with some fish in it. Big orange ones. How about that?"

"Ridiculous," she muttered and went back to her flat, where she sat primly in a deckchair next to her pot of petunias.

A few moments later Mr Price appeared, and began attacking the lawn with an electric lawnmower. Mr Potter stood in the doorway of his hut and glowered. Other tenants appeared and began cheering Mr Price on.

There was, Miss Jevons noticed, an almost festive air about the residents. They had actually started talking to each other since Mr Price had come to live there. Before, they had exchanged frosty "good mornings" on the stairs, and that had been that.

And Mr Price's mentioning a fish pond had brought back another fond memory, of herself leaning down into the cool depths of a pond, bright with white lilies touched with water drops, trying to catch darting orange fish. They had seemed almost like magic to her, at six or seven, as they flashed beneath the heavy green leaves, iridescent in the glistening water.

She remembered even now the feel of the cold water, the warmth of the sun on the back of her head, the shine of her blonde hair as it fell in a long plait over her shoulder. The sound of her mother calling her for tea. She blinked, telling herself not to be so foolish.

But suddenly, she began to long for a pond, and waterlilies, white ones, with little pond insects flitting across the surface and a sparkle of water in the air.

THE next morning Miss Jevons went into her kitchen to make her early morning cup of tea and nearly dropped the kettle with surprise. Perched on her balcony, placidly eating a nut, sat a squirrel.

"Go away!" She beat on the window and it stared beadily back at her, long bushy tail curled round the rail. It looked like a fox fur, she thought with sudden fancifulness. She caught herself up crossly.

What was she thinking of, lately? And she didn't like squirrels, they were rodents. She had never had one on the balcony before — then she remembered Mr Price and the bag of peanuts he'd hung from the trellis, which no-one had been able to make him take down.

Still in her dressing-gown, she went out on to her balcony, and the squirrel disappeared with a flick of its tail. On the adjoining balcony, Mr Price was sitting in the sun drinking coffee. He was wearing his pyjamas, and there was a squirrel on one side of him and two pigeons on the other. He looked benignly across at her.

"Morning, Miss Jevons. It's a lovely day. Care to come for a walk along the beach, crabbing?"

The impudence of it! She bit her lip.

"Mr Price, I will not have this. You are encouraging vermin with your peanuts and bird-seed. I had a squirrel on my balcony just now. I do not like squirrels, they are rodents, and unhealthy. And the birds are also unhygenic . . ." she added.

"Unhygenic?" he took a deep puff on his pipe and waved his arm. All around them were balconies, empty apart from a pristine pot of flowers and a lonely gnome.

"Maybe. But they bring the place to life don't they? With their bright ways and their friendliness. There's not much friendliness in the world, Miss Jevons," he added, and she felt a surprising pang of remorse.

Not once had she welcomed him, she'd hardly spoken a civil word to him — she caught herself sharply. She would not put up with vermin on her balcony, and his washing next to hers, and not having her dustbin emptied because he upset Mr Potter.

"You are disrupting life here, Mr Price," she said coldly, across the gap between their balconies. "In a few short weeks you've upset Mr Potter, and the gardening contractors, and disobeyed most of the rules."

"And," he said with unexpected perceptiveness, "I've upset you, too, Miss Jevons? That right?"

"It is." She squinted at him in the early morning sun. And suddenly it struck her how happy he looked, in his striped pyjamas. She saw the trellis behind him, a riot of colourful climbing sweet peas framing him, and the peanuts, and the row of pots rampant with colour at his feet. Even his deckchair had canvas of bright flowered material.

She looked at her own mundane striped chair, then turned back.

"If I see another squirrel, Mr Price, I will report it to the — the rat catcher."

He grinned, maddeningly. "Environmental Officers, they're called now, I believe, Miss Jevons. You'll find him at the Town Hall," he added helpfully, and Miss Jevons retired, defeated.

A few days later something new caught her eye next door. Mr Price had just erected a huge sunshade, all pink and blue flowers and a huge frilly fringe. It was ridiculous. No doubt he's trying to pretend he's in the Mediterranean, she snorted, and turned her chair round so she faced in the opposite direction.

It was a few days later that she noticed there was a quiet revolution going on. Other balconies sprouted forbidden trellises. Other balconies had peanuts strung across the railing, other balconies sported new chairs and bright flowers.

And Mr Price had taken over the gardening. Below their balcony two small beds of flowers, rampant with scarlet geraniums, had sprung up. Mr Price puttered round the grounds on a mowing machine. Sitting on it, grinning from under an old cap, belching out fumes behind him, he was for all the world like a racing driver.

And other tenants came to their balconies and leaned over, shouting greetings. It was almost like a triumphant royal progress. Everyone was smiling.

Miss Jevons felt a twinge of loneliness. He had been here only a few months and already everyone knew him. She had been here a year and no-one greeted her like that. No-one, in fact, had talked much to anyone else, till Mr Price appeared. And yesterday a complete stranger had stopped her.

"Don't those flats look cheerful," she had said enviously. "Like something out of a travel magazine, with all those flowers, chairs and pots and sunshades."

Miss Jevons had looked, she'd thought it was silly, wasting money on such things. But that evening, as she watered her lonely pot of petunias, she noticed that her balcony looked strangely empty and forlorn compared with the others.

The next day, Miss Jevons noticed that the balcony doors of Mr Price's flat were shut at breakfast-time. No aromatic smell of coffee floated over to her and the squirrel played alone on the railing, looking in vain for peanuts.

It was strange — usually Mr Price kept the peanuts filled to the brim. To her amazement, the squirrel scampered across to her balcony and sat, nose twitching, looking at her. She blinked in surprise.

"Go away," she said faintly. It sat, looking, she thought, lonely, forlorn, hungry. Defeated, she fetched some biscuits and crumbled them. The squirrel ate fastidiously, then a pigeon hovered to land on her balcony. She eyed it rather nervously. She didn't like pigeons either. Then she noticed what beautiful muted colours ringed its neck. It cooed softly. Quietly, she sat in her striped chair watching the bird. It was quite some time before she remembered the washing-up and Mr Price.

The curtains were still drawn. The flat looked empty. Suddenly she was afraid. Maybe he was ill — perhaps he had had a heart attack. If Mr Price was ill, she should tell someone.

Ten minutes later Mr Potter, grumbling, was opening Mr Price's front door with the master key. "He's not ill," he muttered. "Not him. Live till he's ninety, he will, going around upsetting people."

Astonishing herself, Miss Jevons snapped back at him. "If you had any sense you'd have let him help you, Mr Potter. He only wanted something to do. He was probably lonely."

Then she stopped, knowing positively that she was right. He was lonely — and bored. That was why he invented things to keep busy.

She followed Mr Potter into the flat determinedly. To her surprise it was tidy and well kept. It was also quite empty.

"How very odd," she said. "Where can he be?"

SHE found out, in the next post. There was a letter to her from Harry Price.

Dear Miss Jevons,

I have been called up to Wales to see my son, who has been injured in a car accident and is in hospital. As you are my nearest neighbour, I wonder if you would be kind enough to get a key from Mr Potter and water my plants? I would be grateful. I'll bring you back a stick of rock.

Harry Price.

What presumption! All her kindly thoughts of him flew right through the window. Then she remembered the gay splash of colour from the flowers below her balcony, and reluctantly she got the key from Mr Potter.

For the next few days, she watered Mr Price's plants and fed his pigeons. On the fourth day she found herself picking some of his flowers and putting them in a bowl on his table, to make the flat look lived-in. On the fifth day she sat in his bright chair among the rioting flowers on his balcony, watching the squirrel as it sat eating peanuts.

Down below, Mr Potter came out to empty the dustbins righteously, and a little later the gardening contractors arrived, to cut the lawns and move Mr Price's bird bath.

And Amelia Jevons felt a pang of loneliness.

She actually missed Harry Price, and his disreputable clothes hanging next to hers on the line.

She missed the smell of coffee and tobacco wafting across from his

THE HAPPINESS MAN

balcony, his cheery greeting every morning. She shook herself crossly, and went back to her flat to get ready. It was her day for the old people's home.

But on the way, she found herself in the garden shop in the High Street. To her astonishment, she bought some pots for her balcony. And then some bright pink geraniums to go in them. And, greatly daring, she bought a new chair. A wrought-iron one, with curly legs, white.

Most impractical, but — she looked at her balcony later. It did look nice, she thought, smiling.

She was sitting in the new chair the next day, idly drinking coffee, watching the squirrel balancing along her railings, when she heard a familiar voice from the next-door balcony.

"Stolen my squirrel, then, Amelia?" he asked, and she jumped guiltily.

It was Harry Price, dressed in a formal grey suit and, astonishingly, wearing a bow tie. He was waving a bright pink stick of rock at her.

"Why, Mr Price! How nice to see you!" She spoke without thinking, and a timid flush tinged her cheeks. She went on hurriedly.

"But I do assure you, I haven't stolen your squirrel at all. He just — well, I put the peanuts on my balcony for a change, that's all."

"Thought you didn't like squirrels. You were going to report me, if I remember rightly," he said.

"Oh, but — that was before I got to know this one," she said foolishly. He grinned then leaned over his balcony and passed her the stick of rock. He also gave her a long brown-paper-wrapped parcel, which she took hesitantly.

"There you are, Amelia. Brought you a present for looking after my flat. Thought it would cheer up your balcony." He looked at it appreciatively, in all its new glory. "Didn't know you'd done that already!"

Miss Jevons, overcome with surprise, pulled out a large, pink and green flowered umbrella with a white bobbled fringe. A slow smile of delight lit up her face.

"Oh, but it's lovely, Mr Price!" she exclaimed, then hesitated. "Some of us have been thinking, while you were away, that we'd like to form a Residents' Association. With you as Chairman. I wonder — would you like to come and have a coffee with me, and discuss it?"

He smiled at her. "Nothing I'd like better, Amelia. I'm on my way." And he disappeared into his flat.

Amelia Jevons bustled round her kitchen. It was nice to have someone drop in like this. She got out the chocolate biscuits and her best cups and saucers. And maybe, if they did form a Residents' Association, she'd put in a request for a pond, with goldfish and waterlilies.

She might even offer to do Mr Price's washing in her machine occasionally, to help him out.

After all, she thought, an odd anticipation welling in her as she went to answer his knock on the door, one had to be neighbourly, didn't one? □

Welcome Stranger

Complete Story by MARIAN HIPWELL

She had counted the months and days to her son's homecoming. It had never occurred to her he might bring someone with him.

THE day was crisp and bright, and Alicia, turning towards the hall as she heard the familiar rattle of the letter-box, gave a small sigh of pleasure.

She had woken early every morning for the last week, awaiting with pleasurable anticipation the letter from Gary, which must surely have arrived at last.

Yes, there it was, lying crisp and blue on the hall mat, half hidden by two or three white envelopes — thank-you letters, she guessed, from absent friends for their presents.

Stooping, she picked them up, giving her whole attention to her son's letter.

Letters from her son were few and far between, but she'd received one only a few weeks ago, saying that although he wouldn't manage home for

WELCOME, STRANGER

Christmas, he would be there early in the New Year. And he'd be bringing a surprise!

She'd been disappointed at the time that he'd miss Christmas, but she decided she must make the best of it. And they could always celebrate a belated Christmas.

Alicia smiled as she thought of the surprise he'd bring her. Probably some exotic Oriental present – wasting his money on expensive gifts again.

This letter, she knew, would confirm his arrival — he would have let her know sooner if he had been unable to fulfil his promise.

Having feasted her eyes on the familiar handwriting, as if to satisfy herself that the letter really was from him, Alicia resolutely thrust it into her apron pocket, and catching up the other mail, retraced her steps to the kitchen. She would open these first, keeping the best to last — a habit of hers which Jim had often teased her about.

But even as she read the other letters her thoughts turned to her beloved son, so far away in Singapore, yet so near to her heart.

They had been close, Gary and she, particularly so since Jim had died five years ago. Despite his charming, even slightly irresponsible manner, Gary at 27 had been a tower of strength during that awful time and she had come to rely on him more and more.

She and Jim should have had more children, she knew. If they had, the burden of easing his mother's loneliness would not have fallen so heavily on Gary's shoulders.

Nor would it have been so bad for both of them when his firm suddenly decided to send him to Singapore for three years to supervise the setting up of their new plant. As one of their brightest young engineers slowly climbing the ladder of success, he could not afford to turn down such a brilliant opportunity. It would help his promotion prospects, too, when he returned to Britain.

Sighing, Alicia allowed her thoughts to dwell in the past.

She remembered only too well how devastated she'd been at the news, although she had never let Gary see it.

The weeks leading up to his departure had been almost as much of an ordeal as Jim's death, yet she'd sent her son off with a smile on her lips for all the world to see and an ache in her heart that had never seemed to leave her.

All she could do was look forward to the day when he would come home, meanwhile trying to fill her life with other activities, carrying always the picture of her laughing-eyed son at the other side of the world in her heart.

And then he'd written, telling her he hoped to be home just after Christmas, and as the time grew nearer she had gradually regained some of her old sparkle.

Her son was coming home, and as the letter confirming it nestled in her apron pocket, a glimpse of red caught her eye.

WELCOME, STRANGER

A small sign of satisfaction escaped her as she turned her head to the window. It had bloomed, as she had known it would.

She smiled as she remembered how, on the day she had first received the news, she'd gone out and bought a small cutting of the Christmas cactus, placing it in the sunlit kitchen window, a daily reminder of what was to come.

She'd nurtured the plant continuously, determined that it would flower for Gary's homecoming, and it had become a kind of talisman to her.

The flower would bloom; Gary would come home for Christmas. It was a simple, almost superstitious philosophy, yet it had helped her through the months of waiting.

But it hadn't bloomed quite in time for Christmas. It had waited, as if it knew . . .

With hands that were not quite steady, she ripped open the envelope, suddenly eager to know for certain that soon her son would be with her.

Happily she began to read and it was only as she turned the first page that her smile faltered, to be replaced by an expression of incredulous amazement, followed just as quickly by a small choking sound of disappointment.

Oh, Gary was coming home, all right, but it wasn't to be, as she had so fondly expected, just the two of them — he was bringing a girl with him . . . his wife.

Slowly now, Alicia re-read the words her son had written: We decided suddenly to get married now, rather than later, he wrote in his careless scrawl. I wanted so much for you to meet Sula.

I know it will be a shock, coming like this at the last moment, but her parents would not hear of her coming any other way.

Things are done that way here, Mum. It's hard enough for them to accept that Sula isn't going to marry one of her own countrymen, so we had to respect their wishes, although I'd much rather the wedding had taken place in England, with you there.

I know you'll be disappointed that there wasn't time to get to know Sula first; but when you meet her, you'll love her on sight, just as I did.

I was going to keep the news as a surprise for you till you met her, but Sula persuaded me to prepare you in advance.

Give her a chance, Mum, that's all I ask. For my sake, please.

He had enclosed a snapshot of Sula, yet at first Alicia could hardly bring herself to look at it.

When she did, she saw that her daughter-in-law was beautiful.

Her classic Eurasian features were enhanced by dark, friendly eyes and a warm, gentle smile. He would have fallen in love with her at once, Alicia knew.

She had realised long ago that that would be the way it would happen. Girls had come and gone before he'd left for Singapore, but she'd somehow known that they meant nothing to him.

Yet she knew him; knew that one day he'd meet a girl and that would

WELCOME, STRANGER

be it. Only, she'd always imagined she would have had time to get to know her future daughter-in-law, to accept the fact that she must now come second in her son's affections.

But this way . . .

A little angrily now, Alicia thrust the thin sheets back in the envelope. The girl, however charming, was a stranger to her, intruding on the special time she'd so looked forward to.

Slowly she stood up, taking her coffee cup over to the sink. Determinedly, she averted her eyes from the window-sill.

The Christmas cactus, blooming at last, seemed to mock her. So much for your talisman, it seemed to say. What will you do now? They'll be here in two days, so you haven't much time.

There was nothing to do, in fact. The turkey and the mince pies needed only to be defrosted; the Christmas cake nestled in its box, already iced.

She'd been determined to make his homecoming just like a traditional Christmas, and had even left up some of the decorations, ready to signal a welcome to Gary — Gary, and the stranger who was his wife.

Alicia turned away from the sink, her mind suddenly going back over the years to her own difficult first year with her mother-in-law.

It had seemed, to her youthful mind, that Jim's mother resented her, disliked her for taking her son away from her, and it had only been Gary's birth which had made her realise that what she'd taken for hostility was simply insecurity, a feeling of being threatened.

All that had fallen away when Jim's mother had looked down at her first grandchild. It had taken a baby to bring them together, and Alicia had vowed it would not be that way with her daughter-in-law when the time came.

Yet now she felt everything her mother-in-law must have felt; the pain, the feeling of loss, of being unwanted.

Suddenly, Alicia wished the festive season many months away. It was a time for love and charity, and she felt none of these things, only hurt, unreasonable anger at Gary.

Yet, why should she, she reasoned. He was a grown man, perfectly free to marry, and if she was a little hurt that she had been left in ignorance, well, the circumstances had dictated the event.

What right had she to feel jealous? She'd had his love and care for 27 years — it would be selfish to ask for more.

And was she being unfair, too, to the girl. She was coming half-way round the world to meet her husband's mother and deserved a warm welcome with no reservations. But somehow that seemed impossible. Alicia turned away, suddenly sick at heart.

The day dragged on. Alicia performed her household tasks almost mechanically, heavy hearted, her eyes straying every now and then to the letter she'd thrown on to the table. Little absurd thoughts invaded her mind.

Suppose she hadn't opened it. Suppose it had gone astray . . .

But commonsense told her that pretending things were the same was futile. Better to try to accept . . . And she was such a lovely girl.

Alicia could understand how her dark beauty, the eyes so full of warmth, had caught at Gary's heart. For his sake, she had to pull herself together and accept the situation.

For Gary's sake — and her own.

S HE was sitting at the fire, knitting, trying to calm her thoughts, when a sudden shadow through the window caught her eye. That familiar figure could only be Gary.

All else was forgotten in her desire to see her son, and she had reached the door even before he'd had time to ring the bell.

He had changed, she could see that at once. His face, though deeply sunburnt and smiling, had a new maturity which had not been there before.

"Hello, Mum!" he said simply.

With a sob, she rushed towards him, holding him to her as if she'd never let him go. He stroked her head, slightly embarrassed, then as she held herself away from him, he shook his head.

"Hey, why the tears, Mum?" he teased gently. "I'm home again. Give me a smile."

Impulsively, she smiled, spreading her hands in bewilderment.

"But — you said Thursday —" she began.

"Caught an earlier plane!" he said, grinning. "We couldn't wait any longer to see you — either of us!"

At that, Alicia sobered and, remembering, glanced around.

"But where —" she began.

"She's at the hotel," Gary said quietly. "I've just left her there."

A cold spasm touched Alicia's heart, and she looked at him uncomprehendingly.

"But you — you're staying here, aren't you?" she stammered, hardly aware of the pleading note in her voice.

"Of course we are!" Gary was quick to reassure her. "Where else?"

Stepping inside the house, he dumped his suitcase and looked at his mother. "It's good to be home," he said gently.

Alicia's mind was in a whirl. "But why . . . ?" she said at last.

Taking off his overcoat, Gary took her arm and led her into the sitting-room.

"Let's have a cup of tea and then we can talk," he said firmly.

Automatically, she obeyed. Something must have happened. Sula

WELCOME, STRANGER

didn't want to see her after all . . .

Her hands were shaking visibly as she handed him a cup and seated herself across from him, waiting . . . He returned her gaze steadily.

"Sula wanted us to have this time together," he said finally. "She felt it would be wrong of her to intrude on our first hours. After all, we've been apart so long.

"She insisted I book her in at a hotel for tonight, then bring her here tomorrow," he added. "She explains it in this note."

Handing her a small envelope, he watched, aware of her still shaking fingers as she slit the envelope open and began to read. The writing was as neat and orderly as Gary's was careless.

Dearest Gary's mother,

I so long to call you my own mother but feel it would be presumptuous of me. I wish for you to have your special time with your son for which I know you must have longed so much. It is only right that it should be so.

Tomorrow, if it pleases you, I will come. I hope very much that you look forward to meeting me and I hope we will be friends.

With kindest regards and already love.

Sula.

There was silence for a while as Alicia digested the note, a lump rising in her throat. "She's very thoughtful," she said at last, her voice soft.

"She's a very special girl," Gary said quietly. Reaching across, he squeezed her hand. "Just like you, Mum."

"But it's impossible!" Alicia said, suddenly agitated. "She can't spend her first night all alone in a strange country! We must bring her here, Gary."

"No, Mum," he said gently, "please don't go. This is her gift to you — the only one she has to give. Don't throw it in her face."

Alicia looked at him for a long time.

"You're right," she said then. "Of course you're right." Sitting back in the comfort of her chair, she looked across at the mistletoe. "Childish, I know." She laughed. "But I so wanted you to have all the trimmings." Her voice trembled suddenly. "I expect you'll be going back soon enough."

"Yes," Gary agreed, "but it's only for another year, Mum. And we want you to come out to us in the spring for a long holiday. Sula's longing to show you her country — and it is beautiful, you know."

There was so much Alicia wanted to know, but first . . .

"How long have you known her?" she asked carefully.

"Not very long." Gary smiled. "But I feel as if I've known her all my life."

Alicia remembered the feeling. Even now, over 30 years later, it was still with her.

They sat in companionable silence for a while, then talked of the past, the present, the future. It seemed they would go on for ever, so much had they to say to each other.

As they talked, Alicia felt her unease gradually quieten, her sadness turn to acceptance and a sort of contentment.

Watching her son's face as he talked, she could see his happiness and she knew who was responsible.

They sat for hours, talking, remembering, as they ate a meal on a tray in front of the fire.

Then, Gary caught sight of the Christmas cactus on the windowsill where Alicia had moved it to welcome him.

"That's beautiful!" he said in surprise.

Alicia's eyes followed his. "I bought it months ago," she said quietly, "when I first knew you were coming home for Christmas. I wanted it to bloom for your homecoming and it has done.

"It's a good omen," she added involuntarily.

Gary smiled. "Thank you," he said quietly.

Alicia suddenly jumped to her feet. "My goodness, look at the time, we must go to Sula.

"I want to thank her for her gift," she added in a gentler voice, "and it is time, isn't it, that she came home?"

Somehow, she wasn't surprised to find she meant it.

Gary nodded. "If you're ready," he said, looking directly at her.

Alicia's reply was firm. "I'm ready," she answered. "I want to meet my daughter-in-law now."

Alicia went into the hallway, reaching for her coat, as Gary waited by the door. Opening it, he looked out.

"It's snowing," he said, quiet satisfaction in his voice. As Alicia joined him in the doorway, large flakes fell softly to the ground, making no sound as they settled on the rooftops, on the branches of the trees, already transforming the landscape, giving the familiar fairy-tale look to it all.

"She's so looking forward to seeing snow," he murmured, half to himself, "she'll be running round the hotel grounds like an excited child now." Smiling, he tucked his arm into Alicia's.

"Just like old times, eh?" He grinned. "Just you and me walking in the snow as we used to do."

With these words, the very last of Alicia's unease melted and she was content. Silently, she wished the past goodbye and saluted the future. A future which did not seem so threatened after all . . .

"Just a minute. I've forgotten something," she said suddenly.

Sula's gift, small in material terms, but priceless and infinitely precious, elicited some sort of response; something a tinsel package could not say.

Swiftly, Alicia returned to the sitting-room and picked up the Christmas cactus.

Then, finding pen and paper, she wrote a short note. "To my daughter, Sula," she murmured aloud. "Welcome — and a Happy New Year."

Tucking the note into the side of the plant, she put both into the bag and, turning towards the door, stepped out into the night, where her son awaited her. □

Complete Story by
CAROL MARSH

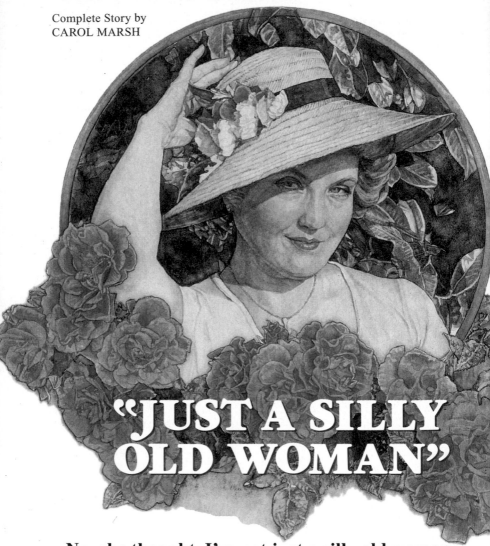

"JUST A SILLY OLD WOMAN"

**No, she thought. I'm not just a silly old woman.
I'm also happy and alive — and in love!**

DOROTHY PRESTON walked along the beach towards the
railway station. The sea breeze ruffled her newly-washed grey hair
and blew back the folds of the soft, blue trouser-suit that set off
her trim, 62-year-old figure.

In her heart, excitement soared wildly, like a song.

Why can't you be sensible, Mum? As she trudged over the damp sand, she seemed to hear the quiet, well-modulated voice of her married daughter, Sheila, trying hard to keep impatience under control — just as Dorothy now tried to control the strangely-mingled hopes and doubts in her mind.

"So you and this Ted kept each other company while he was here on holiday," Sheila had said. "That's fine. I'm all for you having a good time.

"I know life hasn't been easy for you since Dad died. But, well, all good things come to an end, Mum —"

"— And holiday romances are as crazy and intangible as sandcastles?" Dorothy had retorted. "I know, I know . . ."

Dorothy shook her head at her thoughts. She glanced at her watch and quickened her pace.

If Ted had got his times right, the train from Manchester should be coming in within the next 15 minutes.

Her heart quickened at the thought of the kind and cheerful, deeply-sensitive man, three years her senior, whom she had met and grown to care for in the space of his three weeks' holiday from the city, a month ago, now.

Her cheeks flushed as she remembered how they had met — coincidentally, near this very spot on the beach, when, sheltering from a shower of rain, he had looked up from his newspaper as she dodged into the wooden shelter.

She'd been wearing her best coat, she recalled, nothing light and frivolous, like the trouser-suit, but heavy and traditionally sensible camel.

"Not a day for taking a dip," he'd remarked, looking up with honest blue eyes, and Dorothy had looked towards the grey, icy North Sea, and shuddered.

"Not likely! I just like to look at it from a distance, nowadays . . ."

Sadness had flooded her, as, almost instinctively, she'd recalled scenes from Sheila's childhood, before her husband Bob died.

Then, there'd been picnics on the beach, no matter what the weather — and giggly splashes in the cold, spume-tossed water.

How long ago it all seemed.

She'd come back to the present with a start, realising the stranger with the newspaper was watching her almost compassionately, as if he could read her thoughts — or at least the mood of them.

"I was saying — you live here, then?" he'd asked, interested. "You're not just on holiday, like me . . .?"

"No." With a smile, Dorothy had sat down on the bench.

Right from the start, in spite of all she believed — all she had instilled into Sheila about holiday friendships as a teenager — Dorothy found it almost uncannily easy to talk to Ted Downing.

Before she realised what was happening, she was telling him all about Bob's tragic death from a heart attack, 10 years before. Then how her whole purpose in life since then had been to successfully bring up their only daughter.

"JUST A SILLY OLD WOMAN"

"Of course, I was lucky. I had the house, though it's too big for me now Sheila's married and has a baby of her own . . ."

As the rain stopped, she'd found herself moving out of the shelter with the neatly-dressed man, and accepting his offer of a cup of tea at the nearby beach café, as if it were the most natural thing in the world.

"And until I had to retire at sixty, I had my secretarial work at a local firm . . ."

DOTTY! Hey — up here!" The sudden, shrill voice cut into Dorothy's thoughts. Startled, she looked up and her heart plummeted, guiltily, as she saw her best friend, Madge Taylor.

"Come on up!" Standing at the head of the steps up to the pavement, her huge figure accentuated by the wind, Madge looked indomitable.

"You'll ruin your shoes!" she scolded, and then, peering at Dorothy through her imposing black spectacles — taking in the blue trouser-suit, the softly-natural hair — "Going somewhere special, are we?"

Ever since their schooldays, innumerable years ago, Madge had insisted on referring to Dorothy in the plural.

Looking at her now, aware of the suspicion dawning in her grey eyes, Dorothy wanted, quite irrationally, and probably unkindly, to say, "I'm going to the station to met the man I'm going to marry. And please — my name's Dorothy . . ."

Her insides melted as she thought of how it had taken Ted to make her aware of her name.

He was the only person to have used it in full since her father died, because even Bob had shortened it affectionately to "Dodo" , or "Dot".

"Don't let people shorten it," Ted had insisted, after she nervously introduced him to Madge, five days after they'd met and fallen so headlong — so alarmingly — in love.

"It's a lovely name. You'll always be Dorothy to me . . ."

"Dottie Preston — you haven't heard a word!"

Madge's voice dragged her unwillingly back to the present and she blinked in the morning sunlight.

"I said — once the silly season's over, and most of the tourists have gone home, we can all get back to normal.

"Still, there's the woman's club fête on Saturday — don't forget."

"What? Oh, yes."

How could she tell Madge — any more than she had been able to tell Sheila that — irrational though it might be — things would never be "normal" for her again?

That since she met Ted and they made their plans, everything had suddenly come alive for her? Alive and meaningful in a way they hadn't been since she was very young, and Bob's bride.

Her doubts returning, she remembered how she'd tried to explain to her old schoolfriend how the two of them felt, and what they had planned.

Madge had simply snorted with laughter.

"He'll come back here and settle? I've heard that one before!

"And to be quite honest, Dottie, I think you're crazy to even think of putting your house up for sale — too big or not — on the strength of it all.

"What do you know about this man, after all?"

Was she crazy, like Madge said . . .? As she muttered something about being in a hurry, and left her friend in mid-sentence, Dorothy thought with fresh uncertainty of the sign now outside her house. And the changes it stood for.

Looking back along the beach, she remembered how she and Ted had walked there, those wonderful three weeks, hand in hand, talking about the new future that seemed like a fantastic bonus to both of them.

"It's been nearly fifteen years since my Ellen died, and I never thought I'd be happy again." She remembered Ted's voice, husky with emotion.

"We were never lucky enough to have youngsters, so although I've got a good pension, and a little nest egg saved, there's nothing to keep me in Manchester except a grotty little council flat I can give up at a couple of weeks' notice . . ."

"My holiday's over now," he'd said at the station that day, when, her heart aching, she'd seen him on to his train. "But I'll be back, love, I promise.

"I'm not much of a one for letters, but give me a month to sort everything out — sell my stuff and so on, and I'll be back. For keeps . . ." She hugged him.

He'd taken his diary out of his pocket, and together they'd chosen a time.

"Half past twelve on Saturday, August 4th. I'll book in at the Crest Hotel.

"Meanwhile, you get on with the inquiries at the registrar's office, and the house agents. And put the feelers out for one of those headland flats . . ."

Once more, as Dorothy reached the station, she glanced at her watch. Her heart thudded. It was half past twelve now!

"Excuse me." She stopped a porter with a luggage trolley. "Where should I go to meet the Manchester train?"

"The one due in now?" He glanced at his watch. "You'll be best to stay here by the ticket barrier, ma'am.

"All the passengers have to come through this gate."

With a nod of thanks Dorothy began her vigil.

To stop the jangling of her nerves, she concentrated on all the things she had to tell Ted when he arrived.

How she had made a tentative date for them at the registrar's office, and had looked around the flat they'd set their hearts on, and found it perfect.

"But, Mum — it's ridiculous!"

As she heard the rumble of an approaching train, she thought again of

"JUST A SILLY OLD WOMAN"

Sheila, and her perfectly reasonable arguments.

Arguments she couldn't help but echo a little in her own hopeful, fear-filled heart, now the time had come.

"You'll be two strangers marrying — and apart from that, well, those flats you're talking of buying might be luxurious, but they're so — well — small.

"And you know how I rely on you to have Shane for me, weekends . . ."

Dorothy wondered why, out of all Sheila's objections, that last one should stay in her mind.

She recalled her daughter's flushed face when her young husband, Brian — the one person who, unexpectedly, seemed to see Dorothy's point of view in all this — had pointed out that maybe "Ma" didn't want to have her baby grandson, adorable though he might be, to stay every weekend.

Maybe — just maybe — there were other things she'd prefer to do with her free time, now and then . . .?

Things like walking along the beach with the man of her choice — in no hurry, contented and free. With the day at their disposal, and a happy dog dancing at their heels.

She came out of her thoughts then, as a swell of passengers began to come through the gate by the ticket barrier. Soon she should see him.

Straining eagerly forward, she waited until the swell became a trickle, then realising that Ted was late, she pushed down her flush of anxiety with another memory.

"As soon as we're married, we'll get a dog . . ." he'd said excitedly, standing up to stretch after an impromptu lunch on the sands.

"It'll keep us company in our old age — and make sure we don't get too houseproud in our posh new flat . . ."

"A nice, big dog no-one else wants." Dorothy had felt her "old age" was centuries ahead, as she took his warm hand in hers.

"I've always wanted one, but, well, after my husband died, I was out at work all day, and since I've been on my own, it just hasn't seemed worthwhile somehow . . ."

"Everything's going to be worth while from now on, Dorothy. We've both got years ahead of us, and we can make sure they're golden ones with each other . . ."

 Continued on page 94

TEDDY

It's Christmas time,
know how I can tell?
I saw silver stars and a
bright golden bell,
Bright parcels all done
up with ribbons and
bows,
While outside the
window it snows and it
snows.

There's a tree in the
living-room smelling of
pine,
And behind the chair
there are bottles of
wine,

From the mantelpiece
stockings hang in a row,
And tied round my neck
is a red and green bow.

It's peaceful right now,
but what's that I hear?
A cry of, "He's been"
and a resounding loud
cheer,
Hold on to your hats,
the children are coming,
Hurry up, kids, I'm here
for the cuddling.

Phew, what a lovely day
it has been,

We sat after dinner
watching The Queen,
We wore silly hats and
had lots of play,
It really was a wonderful
day.

Now it's late and
everyone's sleepy,
The children are tired
and feeling weepy,
But I'm raring to go, I'm
fit and I'm ready,
It's what I do best, I'm a
comforting teddy

T. Ashby

"JUST A SILLY OLD WOMAN" *Continued from page 92*

Dorothy blinked as she seemed to hear the echo of his soft Northern voice, trembling with sincerity.

Then she started, coming back to the present with a jolt as she realised all the passengers from the Manchester train seemed to have gone through the barrier now. And there was absolutely no sign of Ted among them.

Puzzlement rising in her, she looked around, and saw the porter she had spoken to before.

"Excuse me," she said again, her voice, even to herself, sounding hollow with dawning fear, "but — but is that all the passengers from the Manchester train?"

He looked at her, and she turned away from the momentary knowledge and sympathy she saw in his eyes.

"I think so, ma'am," he said, "but I'll check the platform for you."

DOROTHY knew, even before he came back and shook his head, that the platform was deserted. She stood there, as if turned to stone. She couldn't believe Ted hadn't come, and as she looked again at the station exit, she felt pain and crushing disappointment crystallise inside her.

Catching her breath, she tried to sort out her numbed emotions. There must be some mistake!

Maybe — maybe she'd got the date or the time wrong — or Ted had simply missed the train at the other end?

And just then, as if to verify her thoughts, the railway Tannoy crackled into life.

"We have a message for Mrs —" Dorothy's heart lifted, not daring to beat for hope and longing as she strained her ears.

"— Martin," the voice went on, uncaringly giving the name of some stranger. "Could you please report to the station-master's office . . .?"

As the sea breeze seemed to turn to wind, whipping loose sand across the pavement, Dorothy turned brokenly away, other voices echoing now in her heart.

Madge's vigorous, The silly season's nearly over, Dottie! And Sheila's cool, young insistence. Don't be ridiculous, Mum!

Ridiculous.

Suddenly, that was exactly how Dorothy felt, out on a Saturday morning, waiting for a stranger she hardly knew, and, quite obviously, would never see again. She suddenly felt older.

The blue suit, bought especially because he'd admired it in Dawson's window, suddenly seemed pathetic and incongruous.

There was, after all, no fool like an old fool, Dorothy concluded, as she turned from the station and began to walk slowly home. Everyone had been right.

Ted, and all he'd told her those weeks, had been a fantasy. A holiday romance no different from those enjoyed and then cried over by Sheila and her friends when they were teenagers.

Only she wasn't a teenager. She was old enough, by far, to know better . . .

The spring in her step gone, Dorothy brushed the loose sand off her shoes, and began to walk back along the pavement.

The beach was now cold and alien. The nip in the air told her that autumn was on its way.

Tomorrow, she thought, blinking back her tears as she tried to plan, she'd cancel the sale of the house, and collect the holding fee on the flat. Nothing had been definite, anyway.

She'd ring Sheila and say she was still available, after all, to have Shane weekends.

As for Madge, she'd go round to see her, in a day or two, and make the arrangements for their round of coffee mornings, and women's club meetings.

She had been a fool — a blind, vain fool — to think that life could hold anything else, at her age.

"Dorothy! Dorothy — wait!" The hoarse shout reached her just as she was about to turn the corner away from the sea front.

She turned slowly, uncertainly blinking, and then, to her amazement and joy, she saw the figure. A long, running figure that, from a distance, could have been that of a young man.

"I shouted and shouted," Ted gasped as, reaching her at last, he caught her by the hands. She saw his eyes were shining, his face, still tanned from his recent holiday, beaming.

"I was late getting off the station, because there was a kiddy lost on the platform — breaking his little heart he was, because he'd wandered among the passengers away from his mum.

"Anyway, by the time I'd calmed him down, and they located his mother, I realised you hadn't come to meet me . . ."

"I — I thought you hadn't come," Dorothy confessed, hanging her head. "When the porter said you weren't on the platform, I —"

"I must have been in the station-master's office by then," Ted said softly. "I took the kiddy there.

"Did you really doubt me, Dorothy?"

Gently he pulled her close, making a comforting sound, and she realised what his presence meant to her.

"I — I thought you'd changed your mind — that it was all a kind of dream . . ."

Softly he kissed her, and she knew, if she'd needed any more telling, that everything was going to be all right.

That, crazy though it might be, she was safe — as if she'd come home from a long, wearisome journey.

"This dream, my love," he said tenderly, "is going to come true — because we're going to make it! Now — how about going for a nice cup of tea . . .?" □

Complete
Story by
ISOBEL
STEWART

NOT THE MARRYING KIND

**At least that's what he thought. His mother? Now
she had very different ideas . . .**

MARRIAGE, Robert James Watson told his mother when he was
22 years old, was all right for some people, but not for him. He
wasn't the marrying kind. He wasn't interested in family life
and, besides, he took the population explosion much too seriously to
consider adding to it.

His mother, a very restrained lady, only said wistfully that surely one
or two grandchildren for her wouldn't make that much difference.

Rob had an answer for that. She already had two grandchildren and
one on the way — thanks to Rob's sister, Sue, and her husband, Steve.

And to be fair, the arrival of Katy three months later, her first
granddaughter, did keep his mother pretty satisfied. But a few years after
that, when Katy was four and Rob was 26, the question arose again.

"Sue says in her letter that she and Steve enjoyed having you for the long weekend," his mother said brightly one night when Rob was having dinner with her. "She says that the boys and Katy miss you very much."

"I miss them," Rob said truthfully. "They're nice kids. Noisy but nice."

"You were a noisy child yourself," his mother said dismissively. She sighed and put her hand over her heart, and Rob thought, affectionately and not for the first time, how much the stage had lost when his mother had married his father.

"It really grieves me, Robert, to see a man like you, who would be such a good father, missing out on such a wonderful experience."

"I do pretty well with a share of Sue's kids," Rob said lightly.

"It isn't the same," she told him firmly, and tragically.

Rob went on eating.

Not to be defeated, his mother changed tactics. "I enjoyed meeting Hilary the other night. Does she — er — drop in often?"

"Fairly often," Rob replied. "She lives right across the hall."

"She's very attractive, don't you think?"

"Very," Rob agreed. "She's intelligent, too — has a good job in an advertising agency."

"I'm not against working wives," his mother said, "although your father would have been shocked." She sighed. "He would be very disappointed to think of no grandson to carry on his name."

Rob put down his fork. "Mother," he said firmly, "that just isn't fair."

"No, I don't suppose it is," she agreed. "Rob, how about bringing Hilary over for dinner?"

"Thanks, I'll do that," Rob replied. "But it doesn't mean I plan to marry her." He looked pointedly at his mother. "Besides, I'm sure Hilary feels the same as I do about marriage."

"Nonsense, Robert, I won't have you talking that way!" For a moment Rob had the absurd conviction that if he did, he wouldn't get any dessert.

"How do you know how Hilary feels about marriage? I'm sure you haven't discussed it with her."

NO, Rob hadn't, but he knew that if he told Hilary about this conversation with his mother, she would laugh — with the delicious, gurgling laugh she had. Then she'd agree with him that, of course, she wasn't the marrying kind, either.

And Hilary did laugh. She threw back her head and laughed, her brown eyes sparkling with amusement, and Rob thought how nice it would be to have that silvery laughter ringing through his apartment more often.

"Oh, Rob, you dear funny boy," she said at last.

No-one, not even his mother, had ever called Rob a dear funny boy. He smiled, but a little uneasily. "You feel the same, don't you?"

"No," she said. "I don't." Her mouth closed and Rob noticed for the first time what a determined chin she had. More than determined — stubborn.

NOT THE MARRYING KIND

"I believe in marriage," Hilary said with conviction. "Some day I'm going to marry a man I love and we'll have children and a dog and even an apple tree in the back garden."

For one incredible moment the picture was there. Rob saw Hilary, sitting under an apple tree with a little girl beside her and a dog lying asleep in the dappled sunshine. He shook his head and the picture disappeared.

Rob shrugged. "Please yourself," he said, aiming for indifference.

"Oh, I will," Hilary said. She wasn't laughing now. In fact, she wasn't even smiling, but Rob was suddenly sure that the moment she got back to her own apartment she was going to laugh, and go on laughing.

A few nights later, he told his mother, in reply to her question, that no, he hadn't invited Hilary to dinner with them, and as a matter of fact he didn't think he'd be seeing much more of her in the future, except as a neighbour.

His mother looked at him, her eyebrows raised.

"I found out that Hilary and I have some very different ideas about things," he said stiffly.

"Ah!" his mother said with satisfaction, and much to Rob's surprise, she said nothing more.

Hilary never mentioned the subject of marriage again either. She asked him to dinner once the next week and he accepted, telling himself firmly that it was foolish to feel disappointment because there were four other people there as well.

A few days after that, Rob came in from work just as the telephone began to ring. It was his mother.

"I've got the children with me. That was Katy," she said unnecessarily, as a loud feminine yell hit his eardrums. "Sue and Steve have gone away together for a few days. I need your help."

"My help?" Rob asked, alarm bells sounding. "Mother, I don't have room for the kids here."

"I'm not asking you to take them. It's the dog," his mother said distinctly. "Rob, you'll have to come round here as soon as possible."

With that, Rob was left holding the silent receiver. He called back but there was no reply. Dog, she had said. Sue and Steve didn't have a dog.

HIS mother was at the window when he arrived, and before he could reach the door, it was thrown open and his nephews and niece hurtled towards him.

He greeted Michael and then Peter and lifted Katy up, before he noticed a small, wriggling object at his feet.

"What's that?" he asked.

"It's Jessica," Peter said.

Rob had never seen a more unlikely Jessica. She was small and plump and her forehead was furrowed as if she had all the cares of the world to bear. Rob bent down for a closer look.

"She's a spaniel," Peter told him earnestly.

"She's smart," Michael said. "When she grows up she'll love her family and protect us from anybody who tries to get into the house."

Jessica didn't look as if she'd ever be a watchdog, but suddenly her small teeth nipped Rob's ankle.

The children thought this was very funny and they were still laughing when Rob's mother came out.

"There you are, Rob," she said, as if she didn't know he was there.

"I called you back, but you didn't answer," Rob said, accusingly.

"I didn't hear the phone," she said quickly and, he was certain, quite untruthfully. "Now, Rob . . ."

"I told you," he interrupted. "I don't have room for the kids."

"Oh, Rob, you don't need to take the children. I can manage them. But I'm too old to cope with a puppy. You'll have to take Jessica for the weekend."

"Take Jessica," Rob repeated. "I can't take Jessica."

"Of course you can," his mother said briskly. "It will pass the weekend for you."

Rob already had many plans for passing the weekend and he saw them all fading inexorably away. He raised a few more objections, but his mother disposed of them all in the same efficient manner, and an hour later Rob found himself on his way home with Jessica in her basket beside him.

They spent the evening together — Rob watching television, Jessica curled contentedly on his lap. After the news, Rob put Jessica and her basket into the kitchen and started to get ready for bed. He went back into the kitchen in his pyjamas and poured himself a glass of milk, watched all the time by Jessica's bright eyes.

"You're a funny little thing," he told her, patting her head.

He switched out the kitchen light and was just settling down his glass of milk on the nightstand when the first howl rent the air. He froze. It didn't seem possible that this heart-rending and unbelievably loud noise could come from such a small puppy.

As Rob returned to the kitchen and switched the light on, Jessica stopped, in mid-yowl, and somehow switched to small yelps of welcome and joy. Rob sat down on the floor and comforted her.

"Now that you know I'm here, you can go to sleep," he told her sternly. Once again he turned off the light. The howls began immediately and the doorbell rang. Rob picked up Jessica and went to the door.

Hilary's hair was rumpled, her cheeks flushed with sleep. In her blue nightgown, Rob thought, she looked about 12 years old.

"What on earth was that?" Hilary asked.

"It was Jessica," he told her.

"A spaniel," Hilary said in delighted recognition, reaching out to scoop the puppy from Rob's arms.

"I was just going to have a glass of milk," Rob said, opening the door

NOT THE MARRYING KIND

wide. "Would you like some?"

"No, but I would like a cup of tea."

Rob led the way into the kitchen. When the tea was ready, they sat down at the table and discussed the problem of Jessica.

"You could try leaving the light on," Hilary suggested. She looked at the puppy doubtfully. "It might work." With that, she finished her tea, firmly told Jessica to be a good girl, and left. The apartment seemed strangely empty when she'd gone.

Having the light on did make a difference to Jessica. Instead of loud, piercing yowls, she contented herself with sad little sniffs. Rob finally gave up and took Jessica to bed with him. Relieved and exhausted, she collapsed on his chest and fell fast asleep. And so did Rob.

He woke to find the puppy licking his face. He was preparing breakfast when the doorbell rang. Hilary, he thought, with an unaccountable lifting of his heart. But it was his mother, with the three children in tow.

"I forgot," she said, not meeting his eyes.

"Forgot what?" Rob asked.

"The church bazaar," she said. "I'm in charge of the needlework stall and I can't possibly keep an eye on the children while I'm there."

Rob knew it was hopeless to argue.

"All right. They can stay here, but only until this afternoon."

When the door closed behind his mother, Rob and his nephews and niece looked at each other, and Rob sincerely hoped that the delighted and trusting anticipation of the three small faces was mirrored in his own.

But what on earth, he thought, could he do with three small children and a puppy here in the centre of the city?

The doorbell rang again, and this time it was Hilary.

"Hi!" she said. "I thought you could use some help exercising Jessica, but I see you've got help here. I guess you must be Peter and Michael and Katy. Does Jessica like playing ball? We could take her down to the park."

Three small faces lit up.

"I haven't had breakfast," Rob protested.

"OK!" Hilary said. "We'll go down to the park and you can come when you're ready. All right, kids?"

All right it certainly seemed, thought Rob, with a confusing mixture of emotions that he somehow felt he'd better not examine too closely.

Half an hour later, as he crossed the park towards them, he stopped. Hilary was sitting on the grass talking earnestly to Katy. The boys were tossing a ball and the puppy was fast asleep on her back.

Afterwards, Rob was never sure just what happened. Perhaps it was at that moment as he stood watching them, or perhaps a little later when they were all back in the apartment and he and Hilary were alone in the kitchen fixing lunch, that he saw with complete clarity and conviction how absurd his own ideas had been.

Not believe in marriage? Right now the thing he wanted most in the world was to marry Hilary and to have children and an apple tree and even, he thought with a burst of enthusiasm, a dog like Jessica.

"Hilary," he whispered urgently, as she tried to arrange the flowers they'd bought. He spoke softly so the children in the next room couldn't overhear. "I have to talk to you. I was wrong. Completely wrong."

She looked at him, saying nothing.

"I like apple trees, too." He was afraid she would laugh again, and he couldn't bear that. He had to say it all, right now. "Hilary, darling, I love you. Will you marry me?"

"Oh, Rob," Hilary said, not quite steadily. "Oh, yes."

He wanted to say more, much more, but he couldn't think of any words. So he kissed her.

"When you've finished kissing," Peter said, interrupting politely, "could you come and tell Michael he can't take two turns in a row?"

Rob kissed Hilary again, quickly, and then went into the living-room to referee the checker game till lunch-time.

Then he told the children it was time to take them back to their grandmother.

"Will you come?" he asked Hilary.

"If you want me to," Hilary said, and he saw, delighted, that there was a dimple in the corner of her mouth.

"It's funny," Katy said thoughtfully, "how Granny 'specially wanted us this weekend when she had her church bazaar, and then she didn't want to take us with her."

My mother, Rob thought with admiration, is a very clever and very devious woman. He didn't know quite how she thought this would achieve something, but — she had been right.

"Katy," he said, "I think Granny knew this was the perfect weekend to have you. Come on, let's go."

"Don't forget Jessica," Peter said.

"We won't," Rob assured the children. He thought of Hilary in her blue nightgown comforting the heartbroken and bewildered puppy in the middle of the night and his heart filled with tenderness.

"In fact," he said, "when Jessica grows up and has puppies of her own, we might be in line for one." He smiled at Hilary.

"We might indeed," she agreed. □

Complete Story
by Isobel Stewart

Big Boys Don't Cry

Don't they? Not even when they feel so lonely and confused . . . ?

JOHNNY would much rather have had a puppy. Puppies were fun. He could have taken a puppy for walks, he could have taught it to chase a ball, it would have been waiting for him every day when he came home from school.

They said it wasn't fair to Rover, because Rover was an old dog, but Johnny knew that Rover wouldn't have minded. Rover would have had fun with a puppy, too.

You certainly couldn't have much fun with that baby. All it did was lie in the pram and sleep, and when it did wake up it made an awful lot of noise for such a little thing, and then Beth picked it up and cuddled it, and when Daddy was home he picked it up, too.

But Granny was the worst of them all, she even picked it up when it wasn't crying.

Actually, it hadn't been too bad at first, Johnny sometimes thought. He'd

102

known about the baby — Beth and Daddy had told him ages ago. He'd told them then that he'd rather have a puppy, and they'd explained about Rover being old.

Then Beth had said that they were really very happy about the baby, so Johnny had said all right, if they wanted a baby they could have one.

The baby had grown in Beth's tummy, just the way the kittens had grown in Matilda's tummy, and you could hear its heart beating, if you put your head right up close to it.

Johnny had liked that, and he had liked sitting on the couch beside Beth while she knitted for the baby, because she used to tell him stories about when he was a baby, stories about when he grew in his mummy's tummy, too.

That was long, long ago, of course, long before Beth knew them, Daddy and him.

His mummy's name was Margaret and she had died in a bad car accident when Johnny was two. Sometimes Johnny thought he could remember her, but mostly he didn't.

He had a picture of her, of course, and she was smiling, but it was just a picture, it wasn't real, not like Beth was real.

Sometimes, when Johnny screwed his face up hard, he could remember how he'd felt about Beth at first. He hadn't liked her, and he hadn't wanted her around.

He and Daddy had been fine on their own, with Granny coming round to bring them pies and puddings and biscuits.

"You're not my mummy," he had once told her fiercely. "You can't tell me what to do!"

He'd been sorry the minute he said it, because Beth looked sad, but then she had smiled.

"No, I'm not your mummy, Johnny," she had agreed. "But I wish I was. I've always wanted a little boy just like you.

"And — as for telling you what to do — now that I'm married to your daddy, I'm afraid you'll have to accept that I can tell you what to do, when I have to. Like now — when I say you take your wellingtons off at the back door, I mean it. All right?"

"All right," Johnny had agreed grudgingly. "But I won't call you Mummy!"

"I'm not asking you to," Beth had replied, bending down to clean the floor where he'd left mud on it. "I'm quite happy to have you calling me Beth."

Actually, soon after that, when Johnny began to see that it was really quite nice having Beth married to Daddy and living with them, telling him stories when he was in bed, making a super Batman outfit for him to wear for the Sunday school fancy-dress party, putting sticking plaster on his knee when he fell and cut himself, he wished, kind of, that he could say that maybe he would call her Mummy, after all. But he didn't like to, so he went on calling her Beth.

But really, they had all been much happier before that baby came, Johnny thought more and more.

They couldn't go out for picnics any more, or walks on the beach, or up the hill to fly his kite, because the baby had to sleep, or he had to have his bottle, or he had to be bathed.

He looked clean enough to Johnny, but Beth put him in the bath every day, and she sang to him and she spoke to him, and the baby just made silly little gurgly noises back to her.

"He's laughing, Johnny," Beth said one day. "Come and see him."

Johnny went, but he didn't think the baby was laughing. It was just sort of screwing up its little face. Actually, he didn't think the baby looked all that great but everyone else seemed to think it was good-looking. Maybe when it got hair it would look better.

"He's got your nose, Jim," his granny kept saying, and Johnny thought that was the silliest thing he'd ever heard, because Daddy's nose was big, to match his face, and the baby's nose was little, and usually it was red, like the rest of him.

Sometimes it seemed to Johnny that people thought there hadn't ever been such a marvellous baby before, and, if you asked him, it was a lot of fuss about nothing.

He'd never have thought either, that one little baby could make so much work for Beth to do.

There were all these nappies to wash, never mind the other clothes he wore, and when Beth made his bottles of milk, there was such a fuss, with bottles boiling on the cooker, because he mustn't get germs, and then there was all this bathing business.

"A puppy would have been a lot easier," Johnny said to Beth one day, loudly, as she was hanging up a line of nappies.

"You're right, Johnny," Beth agreed, as she pegged up the last white square. She smiled down at him — not very far down, because she wasn't very big, and Johnny was quite tall for just being seven — and she put her arm around his shoulders.

"It's been a tough three months for you, Johnny," she said, and Johnny was taken by surprise. "But there were all the feeding problems, and then he was colicky — I think, though, that we're over the worst.

"I'm sorry I've had so little time for anything but looking after Peter. I've tried, but — anyway, things should be better now."

Johnny knew that she had tried — he felt quite bad, now, when he remembered that Beth hadn't ever skipped reading to him after he was in bed, even if the baby had been needing his bottle, then Daddy or Granny had to feed him.

"It's all right," he muttered, and he kicked a stone on the path.

He thought that Beth must have told his Daddy, because that night, when they took Rover out for his walk, Daddy said much the same.

"You've been very good, son," Daddy said, as they walked around the cricket field with Rover beside them. "Beth's had a tougher time than we expected, but now that we've got Peter's feeding problems sorted out, it should be easier.

"And it will soon be summer, and we'll be able to go on picnics. It will be fun for you, having your little brother to play with." He looked down anxiously.

Johnny didn't say anything. Everyone kept saying that, and actually, he'd believed them, before the baby was born. But it was silly, a big boy like him couldn't play with that baby.

Daddy coughed then.

"About that puppy, Johnny. I'm not promising anything for a little while, but — we'll think about it.

"But — for now, Johnny, I just wanted you to know that we feel bad, Beth and I, about the time she has to spend looking after the baby."

Johnny shrugged.

"Well, someone has to," he said, and his voice came out a little funny. His father looked down at him, and Johnny thought he was going to say something else, but he didn't. Yet somehow, Johnny felt a little better after that.

IT would have been all right if it hadn't been for Mrs Dawson. Mrs Dawson was a friend of Granny's, and she'd been away for a long holiday, so she hadn't seen the baby.

Just about as soon as she came home, it seemed to Johnny, she came round, and she brought another stretchy suit for the baby — blue, for a boy, she said.

When Johnny saw it he thought she should have asked Beth first, because the baby had so many of these things he'd never be able to wear them all.

Just like they all did, she leaned over the pram, and she looked at the baby, and she said he was beautiful, and did he sleep through?

Beth said, yes, he did now, thank goodness, but he had been very colicky.

Mrs Dawson said her Ethel's eldest had been colicky, too, but from three months on he'd been fine, and Beth said thank goodness for that.

Johnny, fed up with all this, fidgeted.

"Can I go across and see if Neil can come out to play?" he asked.

"All right, but take a jersey with you, Johnny," Beth said.

His jersey wasn't in his room, so he went to see if he'd left it in the kitchen. But he stopped at the door, because he could hear that Beth and Mrs Dawson had gone in there, and they were talking. And, right away, Johnny knew they were talking about him.

"So how is His Nibs taking it all?" Mrs Dawson asked, above the sound of the kettle being filled.

His Nibs, Johnny thought scornfully. As if I didn't know that's me.

"All right," Beth said after a moment. "But it's a pity I've had to spend so much time with the baby — I think Johnny feels rather left out."

It wasn't right to stand listening, Johnny knew that, and he was just about to go in, when Mrs Dawson spoke again.

"He should be grateful for what you've done for him, Beth," she said. "And he'll just have to realise that things are different now that you've got a little boy of your own."

Once, when Johnny was much younger, and he and Daddy and Beth were having a picnic a the sea, he'd been paddling, and suddenly he'd stepped into a big hole under the water.

Just for a minute, the water had gone right over his head, and then Daddy had been there, lifting him out and standing him up.

He remembered that now, because he felt just the same. Only — Daddy wasn't here now to lift him out and take away the frightening feeling.

Beth was saying something to Mrs Dawson, but he didn't wait to hear. He forgot all about his jersey, and about asking Neil to come out to play. He felt as if there was something inside his chest and it was so tight and so hard that it was almost bursting.

He didn't want Mrs Dawson to see him and he didn't want Beth to see him, so he ran across to the garage, because he had an awful feeling that maybe he was going to cry.

Of course that was why things were different, he thought. Because he wasn't really Beth's little boy, and that baby was. It had been all right before, Beth had been quite happy to have him there, but now it was different. Now, like Mrs Dawson had said, Beth had a little boy of her own.

Johnny didn't know how long he sat there on the bench in the garage, but

BIG BOYS DON'T CRY

when he heard Beth's voice it sounded as if she'd been calling for a long time. Before he could get up, though, she had come in, and she stood at the door, looking at him.

"Johnny!" she said breathlessly. "Where have you been? I've been calling and calling."

"I've been here all the time," Johnny told her, but he had to take his thumb out of his mouth to say it, and for a minute, he looked at her, waiting for her to say, like Granny did, that surely a big boy of seven didn't suck his thumb.

But Beth didn't say anything. She looked at him for a long time, and then she told him it was a bit late to go and play with Neil now, because Daddy would be home soon.

Sometimes, while they were eating, Johnny looked up and found either Beth or Daddy looking at him. But they didn't say anything, not even when he left one of his hamburgers and some beans, and he was glad of that, because although he didn't think he was going to cry, now, his throat still felt awful funny.

Not funny like when he'd had tonsillitis, but a different funny feeling, all hard, like he'd swallowed something and it wouldn't go down.

It wasn't a nice feeling, and it didn't go away even when Beth read the Horrible Heffalump story to him, or even when she kissed him goodnight.

And when he woke up the next day, it was still there, and it even made his cornflakes difficult to eat.

"Do I have to finish my flakes?" he asked, and he was surprised to hear that his own voice was a little wobbly. "I — I don't feel very hungry."

When he came back from washing his hands, he heard Beth say something about "that stupid woman" and he knew she meant Mrs Dawson, and he knew she'd guessed that he'd heard what Mrs Dawson said.

But it didn't matter, because Mrs Dawson was right.

It was Saturday, and Johnny was glad he didn't have to go to school. Daddy was working, but he would be home at lunchtime, he said, and since it was a nice day, maybe they'd go for a picnic.

"Would you like that, do you think, Johnny?" he asked.

"Yes, thank you," Johnny said politely, and the hard lump in his throat was still there.

Beth kept looking at him anxiously, and he didn't want her to, so he went back to the garage so that he could think about things.

He wondered if he should run away, because he didn't think he wanted to stay here any longer, but he didn't know where he would run to.

And then, while he was thinking about this, he heard the baby crying. Quite loud cries, from the pram under the apple tree. Any minute, Johnny thought, Beth would hurry out, and she would lift the baby and cuddle him, and he would stop crying.

But the baby went on crying, and he sounded quite angry, Johnny thought. After a while, he thought he'd better tell Beth, in case she hadn't heard, although he didn't see how anyone could miss hearing.

Beth was in the kitchen, making sandwiches.

"That baby's crying," he told her.

"I know," Beth said. "But I'm making sandwiches for our picnic."

Johnny looked at her.

"But he's crying," he said again.

Beth went on spreading meat paste on brown bread.

"I'm too busy," she told her. "See if you can get him quiet."

106

"Me?" Johnny said, taken aback.

Beth smiled.

"Yes, you — he's your brother, after all."

"Only my half-brother," Johnny muttered, but she didn't seem to have heard him. And the baby was still yelling, so after a moment Johnny went out the back door, and over to the apple tree.

THE baby's face was scarlet and angry, and his little hands were waving furiously. "Hey, that's enough," Johnny said to him. "Keep quiet." The baby yelled even more loudly.

Johnny put out his hand, and the tiny fist closed tightly around one finger.

"That's enough noise," he told the baby severely.

The baby stopped, his mouth still open, ready for the next yell, Johnny thought, and he looked so funny that Johnny couldn't help smiling. The baby's fingers held on to him even more tightly. It was a funny feeling.

He's pretty strong, for such a little baby, Johnny thought, surprised.

"Peter?" he said tentatively.

The baby smiled. It didn't have any teeth, so it was a funny smile, but it was such a happy smile that Johnny laughed, because he didn't think the baby could possibly know just how funny he looked, with his face still red from screaming, and that big smile.

"You're a funny baby," Johnny told him.

He showed the baby the row of bright plastic lambs skipping across the elastic in front of the pram, and he made them do somersaults, and the baby gave a funny gurgle that Johnny guessed was meant to be a laugh.

He seemed to be quite interested in the lambs, so Johnny left him looking at them, and went back into the kitchen.

"He's quiet now, Beth," he said casually. "But if he cries again, I could go back and speak to him. I think he likes seeing me."

"I'm sure he does," Beth agreed. "It isn't every baby who's lucky enough to have a big brother — he'll probably be a real nuisance to you later. He'll want to follow you around, get you to show him how to do all sorts of things — ride a bike, play football, fish, make model planes."

Johnny shrugged.

"I won't mind, really," he said. "He's my brother, after all. Maybe just being half doesn't really matter."

Beth wrapped up the sandwiches.

"It certainly doesn't matter to Daddy and me," she said quietly. "You're both our boys, and that's all there is to it. There's only one thing, Johnny —"

She hesitated.

"I've been wondering — it's going to be a bit confusing for little Peter, hearing you call me Beth. Do you think you could perhaps call me Mummy?"

Johnny shrugged.

"OK," he said. "Just to make things easier for him — I suppose he's too little to work it out."

He didn't know when it had gone, but suddenly he realised that the hard lump wasn't in his throat any longer.

"Want to help me make a cake?" Beth asked him. "We've just time to get it ready to take with us this afternoon."

"OK," Johnny said casually. "I don't mind."

And then, because he couldn't wait to try it out, he said, "OK, Mummy."

And he didn't mind one bit when she bent and hugged him so hard he could hardly breathe. □

Complete Story by
MARGOT RICHARDSON

KEEPING THE PEACE

... that's what she was supposed to be doing — not stirring up more trouble by falling for another girl's fiancé!

"**S** OMEONE has got to go and sort out your Great-Aunt Fay," Mum firmly announced, one wet morning in October. My father hid himself hurriedly behind the newspaper, and my brother, Peter, suddenly discovered something enormously absorbing in his magazine.

They needn't have bothered. I was the person my mother had fixed her gaze on.

"Linda," she said, "Listen to this —" She was brandishing a letter in Auntie Fay's revolting pink notepaper.

"Dear Susan and family, hope all well. Apart from slight cold, am the same but new doctor so did not bother."

"Does anybody understand what she's on about — or is it just me?" Dad showed a baffled face round the edge of his paper.

"It's quite clear," Mum said, "if you're used to her. Now, where was I?"

She sipped her tea and continued, "Am having problems with new neighbours, young couple, getting married soon, so they say.

"They all do it nowadays — living together — no business of mine. Next month I think it is. Poor Mrs Collins has sold up and moved to Worthing, I am so sorry for her."

"What's she got against Worthing?" Peter said, but Mum shushed him and carried on.

"They have taken away my fence and let the dog out and yesterday it was the blackbird tree. That has been there ages.

"Someone must make them put my fence back. It isn't right when a person's over eighty — that tree's their home. Come the spring they won't have anywhere to nest."

"She's probably got the whole thing wrong," Dad said. "To start with, she doesn't even have a dog."

"Yes, that confused me, too," Mum admitted, as she started to clear away the breakfast briskly, "and she isn't over eighty, she's seventy-eight."

"She's been claiming to be over eighty for the last five years," Dad muttered, folding his paper. "She thinks it'll make people say that she's wonderful for her age."

"I do know the tree, though," Mum called from the kitchen. "It was in Mrs Collins' garden next door, I think. She was always on about the blackbirds."

You'll notice that I have remained silent so far. This is not because I am normally so reticent but because I knew what was coming next and was preparing for evasive action.

"Linda . . ." Mum said persuasively, "Can't you . . . ?"

"No!" I leapt up and prepared for a dash to the safety of my darkroom, down in the cellar.

"But you haven't got anything on this weekend — have you, dear?"

"I've got a lot of printing-up to do, Mum. There's more to photography than just clicking the shutter, you know."

"She obviously needs someone to sort her out and I simply can't spare the time at the moment, and as for your father . . ."

"Don't bring me into it!" Dad looked alarmed.

"I never understand a word she says, and she never remembers who I am.

"It's an excellent relationship, let's keep it that way! Linda is the obvious person."

"She likes Linda best, anyway," Peter smirked. I kicked him.

SO this is why the following afternoon found me standing glumly on Great-Aunt Fay's doorstep, small duffel bag over one shoulder and large camera bag over the other, trying to get in.

Not the easiest of tasks.

"Who's there?"

"It's me."

"I don't want any. Go away."

"Auntie Fay. It's Linda."

"If you're selling those double windows . . ."

"AUNTIE FAY — COME TO THE DOOR!" The door opened a crack, held by a safety chain.

"Oh, it's you, Linda. Why didn't you say?"

KEEPING THE PEACE

"I . . . Oh, never mind. Do you think I could come in — it's a bit wet out here."

"Come in. You're a bit wet."

"It's raining."

"Is it raining?"

I followed Great-Aunt Fay down the narrow hall into the tiny kitchen at the rear.

She talked all the time as she made a pot of tea and cut me huge slices of her delicious home-made raisin bread.

"Last Sunday morning —" she said, jumping as usual into the middle of the story in order to provide maximum confusion. "— first thing. Bang! Bang! Bang! Woke me up. No idea what it was."

"No sugar," I said hastily, trying to stem the flow. "So what was the banging on Sunday morning?"

"I told you." She put two spoonfuls of sugar into my cup.

"It was the tree. The blackbird tree. Mrs Collins planted that before you were born. I could see it from my bedroom window."

I said carefully, "The people who've bought Mrs Collins' house next door have cut down her tree that you used to like and the blackbirds used to nest in."

"That's what I said!"

"Well, it's a shame of course, but you can't complain about it, you know. It is their tree. They can do what they like with it."

Auntie Fay looked at me doubtfully.

"And there's the fence. They've got to put my fence back, surely? And what about the dog? All over the place, it is. Great ugly brown brute. Trampled through all my carefully-tied-up daffodil stalks."

"It's their dog?"

"Of course it is. I haven't got a dog."

"We did wonder . . ."

"I wish you'd concentrate, Linda."

"Yes, Auntie Fay. Sorry." I crossed to the window and peered out through the rain.

The fence had certainly gone and the next door garden, where some sort of building work seemed to be going on, was just a sea of mud.

"You can see the tree that's not there," Auntie said at my shoulder. "What made you think I had a dog?"

I sighed. It was going to be a long weekend.

LATER that afternoon, just as Great-Aunt Fay was preparing an enormous tea, she suddenly stiffened and, pointing out of the kitchen window, began to boil like an over-full kettle.

"There she is!" she hissed. "There she is now. And that awful dog."

"Get out of there, you nasty thing!" she bellowed in my ear.

"Hang on. Calm down." I leapt up in alarm. "You'll break the window hammering it like that.

"I'll go and have a quiet word about the fence and the dog. But not about the tree. There's nothing you can do about that. You stay here."

I went into the garden. Great-Aunt Fay, naturally enough, ignored my last instruction and followed closely behind me.

We marched in step down the path towards the pretty, dark-haired girl who was standing in the mud of her garden with a soppy-looking Alsatian.

"Excuse me . . ." I put on my most pleasant and charming voice — the ingratiating tone I used for complaining in shops —

"Excuse me . . ." I began.

"Hello?" she looked up.

"I'm Linda Chapman. Miss Goodwin is my great-aunt."

"Yes?" She looked puzzled but friendly. "I'm Liz."

"I . . . well . . . it's just that my aunt is a bit worried . . . well, concerned really — about the . . ."

"The tree."

"What tree?" the girl asked.

"No." I shushed Aunt Fay firmly. "We don't want to talk about the tree."

"I do," she added vehemently.

"There isn't anything you can do about the tree."

"What tree?" The conversation was getting distinctly out of hand and the Alsatian, having decided that we were two new friends, was celebrating by digging Auntie's rockery.

But Auntie Fay was unstoppable now.

"Mrs Collins' tree. The blackbird tree. It should be there." She pointed. "They always came to that tree. Next spring they won't have anywhere to build their nest. You had no right . . ."

"I'm very sorry about the birds, but —" Liz had gone bright red with annoyance "— the tree was in our garden."

"It was Mrs Collin's tree." Aunt Fay was not going to be contradicted.

"It was our tree."

"Yes, Auntie Fay. It was their tree." I tried to calm the situation.

"But the blackbirds . . ."

"I'm sorry, Miss Goodwin, but that tree had to go." A stony silence prevailed. It was time I intervened — properly.

"The real problem is — er — the fence," I began.

"Auntie's a bit worried because you've taken her fence down."

"Her fence?" Liz did not look any happier.

"The fence that was here." I gestured vaguely at the muddy strip of earth between Auntie Fay's flattened daffodil stalks and next door's building site.

"I think you'll find," Liz said, and I could tell she was trying very hard to not get really angry, "that the fence which was removed was our fence. Not your Aunt's. Her fence is on the other side of her garden."

She pointed. The dog attacked the other fence enthusiastically.

"If you will look at the fence posts you will see that they are on our side of the fence. That's how you tell whose fence it is."

I hadn't know that small fact, I had to admit. I felt very stupid.

"Oh, I see," I said, quite magnanimously, I thought. "But even so, now there is nothing to prevent your dog from getting into Aunt Fay's garden.

"Surely it's your responsibility . . ." I added tentatively.

"I'm afraid I don't see it like that," Liz replied, and I could see she was angry now.

KEEPING THE PEACE

"If your aunt is worried then it's up to her to keep the dog out of her property . . ."

With that she swept off towards her back door, dignity only slightly impaired by the idiotic Alsatian hanging on to her trouser leg. She turned at the door for a final shot.

"And by the way," she fumed, "she can't shoot the dog unless it's worrying her sheep. Good evening!"

Game, set and match to the lovely lady next door. I trailed back indoors, feeling an utter failure, followed by Auntie Fay wailing, "But I haven't got any sheep . . ."

NEXT morning I awoke to bright sunshine in Auntie Fay's back bedroom. It was a gorgeous day and Auntie was already hovering by the bed handing me a cup of tea and twittering a bit like the dawn chorus.

"First thing," she was saying. "First thing this morning. Bang! Bang! Bang! And the swearing, because he's hit his thumb. Wire everywhere . . . and that dog going mad . . ."

"Wait a minute . . ." I ungummed my eyes and tried to get my brain in gear.

I took the tea. "Start again and try to make it as simple as possible."

"Them next door," she said triumphantly. "Putting up a fence!"

As soon as I was decently clean and dressed I ventured into the garden.

There in the bright sunshine a very nice-looking young man was struggling determinedly with a grate bale of chicken wire and assorted sticks and bamboo canes.

The Alsatian spotted me and galloped over keenly, somewhat hampered by a tangled mess of string. The man looked up.

"Good morning," he said cheerfully. "As you can see, I'm trying to put up a temporary barrier to keep Pythagoras in."

"Pythagoras!" I stared at the dog, who was now being attacked by the string.

"Yes, an unfortunate name, I know. He looked very intelligent as a pup, but he grew out of it.

"I'm Colin, by the way. I gather you're Linda." He stood back and admired his handiwork.

"Not bad, eh?" he said hopefully. "Eventually there will be a proper fence; woven panels; two metres high; concrete fence posts.

"Your aunt needn't worry. Anyway, after the wedding Pythagoras won't be here any more."

I felt a momentary pang for the unfortunate dog. Sacrificed on the altar of domesticity, I guessed.

"You couldn't just hang on to this for me, could you?" Before I knew what was happening I was holding on to the wire as he drove in another stake.

112

"Liz is very sorry she lost her temper, by the way. She isn't usually like that. The wedding's making her a bit jumpy, I'm afraid.

"She should have told you I've been meaning to do this as soon as I had the time.

"Do you think it's more or less straight?"

"No," I said honestly.

So I spent the next hour helping this Colin to erect a temporary fence.

Liz was out shopping, apparently, and though I would have liked to have cleared the air, I couldn't help feeling a bit relieved.

Colin was so pleasant and agreeable that I really enjoyed myself. In fact we both had a lot of fun struggling with the wire, tripping over the dog and generally accusing each other of inefficiency.

I've never been any good at do-it-yourself but I must admit to a certain feeling of pride when, the job completed, we stood back, each on our own side of the fence, and surveyed our handiwork.

"Well . . ." He was more doubtful. "It'll do for now. Thanks for the help, Linda, you were splendid." Really, he had a lovely smile.

"At least it'll keep Pythagoras on his own side of the boundary."

The above mentioned creature was trotting busily up and down the wire, sniffing at it and attempting an occasional surprise attack.

"I think we've done a good job," Colin said, as we shook hands over the wire.

He was still holding my hand when two things happened simultaneously.

Auntie Fay came out of the kitchen and tottered down the path carrying a tray of coffee and biscuits, and Pythagoras, in an all or nothing decision, hurled himself at the wire, just cleared it, dislodged a couple of canes in the process and landed on Auntie Fay.

For an exciting minute the air seemed to be full of hot coffee, flying cups, lose biscuits, excitable dog eating same, and bad language — mostly from Auntie Fay.

When the dust had settled she stood amidst the debris with dignity.

"Young man," she said, giving Colin a withering glance, "you haven't made that fence high enough!"

We spent the rest of the morning making the fence higher and the afternoon filling in the gaps we had thereby created at the bottom.

Colin told me about his job and I talked photography. We laughed a lot and shouted at the dog a lot and it was a very nice day.

In fact, I had to keep reminding myself that he was going to be married soon. He didn't bring the subject up at all — and I certainly didn't.

SUNDAY dawned, bright and clear. I was due to go home that afternoon but I had the morning free. There was no sign of anyone stirring next door, not even the dog, and the fence was still up. I had made it clear to Auntie that there would be a better fence eventually and, apart from the occasional wistful mention of the blackbirds, she seemed to have accepted the situation.

Everything being calm, therefore, I took my camera bag and went out to the nearby park, where I sat on a bench in the playground and took

KEEPING THE PEACE

candid shots of children playing.

I hadn't been there long when I felt a sudden weight on my knee and looked down into the brown eyes of Pythagoras.

"Hello, you soppy thing." I pulled his ears. "What are you doing here?"

"He's with me . . . at least . . . he's supposed to be . . . but he just . . . shot off . . ." Colin galloped up and collapsed on the bench beside me, trying to get his breath back.

I couldn't think of anything to say, so I concentrated hard on focusing the camera on a distant child hitting another.

"Our fence is still up," he said eventually.

"I know." There was a slight pause and I took another shot and pushed the dog's head away from the camera.

"Get down, you stupid animal!" Colin rebuked, then went on, "Your aunt said good morning to me this morning — I think she's forgiven us. She's a nice old thing."

"She's batty." I grinned. "But yes, she's a nice old thing. We're fond of her, anyway."

"I'm sorry about the blackbirds. I didn't know about it being their tree."

"They used to nest there every year," I told him. "That's what she says, anyway. I don't know if it was the same pair or not. They all look the same to me.

"When you're old I suppose you sort of cling on to things . . . look forward to things, like spring and birds nesting. I expect it means you'll see another summer.

"Sorry, I'm beginning to sound a bit maudlin."

Embarrassed, I lifted the camera quickly and tracked a running child, waiting for the right moment to shoot. Colin waited, too. When I had pressed the shutter, he said, "I think she's very lucky to have someone as nice as you to care about her." Then he looked embarrassed, so I hastily changed the subject.

"How about me taking a few shots of Pythagoras?" I babbled — the first subject that came to mind. "Any objections?"

"Good grief, no." He looked pleased. "Love you to. My mother's devoted to the silly beast — she'd love a good picture of him."

It isn't easy to photograph animals and Pythagoras was no exception.

He thoroughly enjoyed the session. First of all he kept jamming his nose up against the lens trying dimly to identify this strange object that I kept waving at him.

Then he knocked me to the ground a couple of times as he tried to attack the camera strap.

Eventually he decided that the camera was something we were going to throw for him to retrieve, and danced about barking furiously because we didn't seem to understand the game.

We had a lively half-hour, during which I shot the dog from various angles — some of them even intentional.

At last we breathlessly gave up.

"I think I've got one or two that might be passable," I said as we left the park.

KEEPING THE PEACE

"Are you coming down to your aunt's again soon?"

"I don't know. I'm fairly busy. I could get a couple of prints to you if they're halfway decent."

"I was thinking, I mean, if you might be coming down . . . it'd be nice to see you again."

"We're bound to bump into each other, as long as you're living next door to Auntie Fay," I said, feeling a bit awkward.

After all, he was getting married in a couple of weeks' time.

I went home that afternoon.

Auntie Fay said she was glad I'd come although she thought I could have been a bit firmer about the blackbirds and did I know the fence was starting to fall down and had I ever known a dog to eat daffodil stalks before?

I said sorry, no, no, in that order and kissed her goodbye, letting her load me down with home-made cakes, and messages for my mother and Albert.

As my father's name is John it gave me something to think about on the train.

THE next day or so felt a bit flat so I occupied myself furiously printing up the last couple of orders I'd had — a very pretty wedding and a rather fat christening.

After that I developed and printed my weekend shots. The children in the park were a fairly poor batch — apart from one shot of a grubby and determined toddler trying to climb up the slide. I was pleased with that.

I had a couple of good ones of Pythagoras which would enlarge up nicely for Colin's mother and an excellent picture of Colin crossly fishing a stick out of the stream, while Pythagoras watched from the side.

By Tuesday I'd cheered up a bit and spent a somewhat fraught evening at the dress rehearsal of the local amateur operatic group, photographing "The Sound Of Music".

Wednesday late afternoon I crawled out of my darkroom, like a mole blinking into the light of day, bribed my brother to deliver the photographs, and fell into a hot bath.

Almost immediately the telephone rang.

"Who is it?" I barked crossly, dripping soapy water on to Mum's best carpet.

It was Colin. I took a deep breath. My pulse rate seemed to be behaving very strangely.

"I wondered how the photos came out."

"Not bad."

"Of Pythagoras?"

"Two of them were rather good. I'll send you . . ."

"Your aunt gave me your number . . ."

"How is she?"

"Fine."

"Good."

"They're good, then?"

"Not bad." The conversation was becoming absurd. Neither of us seemed to know what to say. We were talking in circles.

KEEPING THE PEACE

Suddenly Colin said, "Are you likely to come down?"

And I said — I swear I didn't mean to — "Yes. This weekend."

I could have bitten my tongue off. What on earth was I doing?

I was already too late. He was saying how much he was looking forward to seeing me. That was it. I put the phone down and stared at it.

I SHOWED him the photos of Pythagoras on Saturday, out in Auntie Fay's garden, with our rickety fence between us. Auntie Fay had been pleased to see me again, if a little baffled.

"I thought you came down last week," she said. "Was I wrong?"

Colin really liked the pictures of Pythagoras. In fact, he even called Liz out to look at them. She apologised for losing her temper the weekend before, and reluctantly I had to admit she was really a very nice person.

Then she said something that made me go cold. She asked me if I did weddings.

"Of course she does!" Colin was enthusiastic. "This is, well it was my idea really.

"How would you like to do the wedding? The day Liz here knocks 'em cold in her little white number?"

"I — well . . . I . . . it . . ." I stammered.

"I know what you're going to say. It's too far to come and get the proofs back in time for the reception . . ."

"Yes, yes. That's it!"

"But, it's not." He beamed. "I asked your aunt where you lived — hope you don't mind — and when she told me, well, that's when I got the idea.

"The wedding's no more than a few miles from you — isn't that a coincidence?"

"I wish you'd stop babbling, Colin," Liz said, in rather an embarrassed voice. "Maybe Linda can't make it on that day."

I tried to get a couple of sentences out logically.

"Yes, actually, I'm all booked up," I said. "Every weekend. I'm sorry — I really can't!" And with that I simply fled back into Auntie Fay's kitchen.

There was no way I was going to do Colin's wedding. No way.

I sat sniffling over a freshly-made pot of tea and gave myself a stern talking to. It didn't work.

I'd fallen for Colin like a ton of bricks and I'd no right to, no right at all. I sniffed a bit more and blew my nose hard.

"You're getting a cold," Auntie Fay said. "You always were prone to them as a child.

"Many's a time I've said to Albert . . ."

She left me in the kitchen to answer the front door bell, talking as she went.

I was just going to have to forget him, I told myself sternly, in a couple of weeks he'd be a married man and . . .

Suddenly, Auntie Fay came into the kitchen followed by Colin. She was still murmuring about colds and exactly what she had said to the mythical Albert.

"Sorry to barge in," Colin said. "There's something I've got to show your aunt. Come over to the window, Miss Goodwin."

116

"See — over there? In the conifer beside your shed. Can you see?"

There was a pause, then Auntie Fay let out a long, slow breath.

"Look, Linda."

I joined them. At first I could see nothing, then I saw it, the little black shape, right at the top of the tree. Singing his heart out.

It was a blackbird — his orange beak light against the background. And nearby I saw a flutter of wings — it was the female.

"They've come back," Auntie Fay said. "They've come back — and to my tree this time."

The look on her face was blissful. Colin and I both withdrew from the window and left her to watch in peace.

"I'm glad about that," he said. "Really glad. I've got some binoculars she can borrow if you think she'd like to. She'd be able to see them much . . ."

"She'd appreciate that."

"I'll make sure she gets them before I move out."

It took a few moments for this to sink in.

"Move out?" I said.

"Well, I can't stay here after Liz gets married.

"Pythagoras and I were only lodging with her to keep her company until after the wedding."

"Wait a bit," I said carefully. "I thought you were marrying Liz."

He looked bewildered. "I'm her brother," he said at last. "Didn't you realise that?"

I shook my head slowly. I didn't actually trust myself to speak.

"I know Liz told your aunt about the wedding," Colin said lightly. "I assumed she'd explained about me, too. Mind you, she's been very forgetful lately.

"Anyway, Liz's fiancé's abroad at the moment — that's why I'm here."

Suddenly his expression changed. "So that's why you gave me the cold shoulder." Then in a doubtful tone, he continued, "It was, wasn't it . . . ?"

"Yes," I replied.

"So you'll change your mind about doing the photos for the wedding?" Colin asked.

I tried to sound casual. But there seemed to be several brass bands playing inside my head.

"I might be able to fit it in, after all."

"Look at that dog," Auntie Fay said. Pythagoras could see us all from his position on the other side of the wire and was having hysterics trying to reach us.

Even as Auntie spoke he made one last effort — leaped and landed on top of the wire. He hung on grimly howling while both fence and dog slid slowly to the ground.

"I never did have any faith in that fence," Auntie Fay said triumphantly.

Colin and I started to laugh and somehow, as we laughed, I found his arm round me.

Soon we were clinging together helplessly, giggling as Auntie Fay rambled on about fences, Pythagoras tried to untangle himself from the chicken wire, and the blackbirds fluttered from branch to branch, unperturbed and beautiful. □

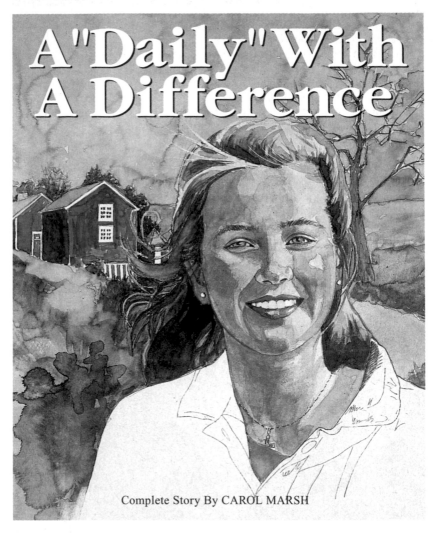

A "Daily" With A Difference

Complete Story By CAROL MARSH

Someone to help with the housework — that's what she had advertised for. Not someone to tidy up her whole life!

I FOUND the first note when I got back from the office on Monday. Dear Miss Harley, it said. Sorry I only gave the living-room a cat-lick, but your bedroom was in a terrible state. Yours sincerely, L. Pedford.

I kicked off my shoes and looked around the living-room. It didn't look

A "DAILY" WITH A DIFFERENCE

as if it had been given a "cat-lick" to me. In fact, it was neater and cleaner than it had been for months.

This agency charlady must be really efficient, I thought, congratulating myself.

Going through to the bedroom, I blinked in absolute amazement.

She'd said it had been in "a state" — and compared with the way it looked now, I realised guiltily, how right she had been.

All my clothes had been hung up in the wardrobe — the dressing-table top was not only visible, but gleamed. And even the spare, framed certificate that proclaimed to the world that I was Victoria Harley, Certified Chartered Accountant, was readable through its glass.

Shedding the good suit and blouse I'd worn for work, I climbed into my jeans (I found them at long last in the bottom drawer of the dressing-table) and pulled a sweater over my head.

It was great not having to worry about cleaning the flat, and as I stretched out in front of the stereo later, with an omelette and salad and a glass of white wine, I wondered why I hadn't thought of getting in some help before.

"It's quite simple, really, Vic," my friend Sonia at the local Women-Unite Group had said, when I complained about how shattered and frustrated I was, after struggling for two hours pushing the vacuum cleaner round the flat.

"Just forget your inbred guilt complex and accept that all people, male or female, should do what they're good at in this life. And in your case, that's chartered accounting, certainly not charring . . ."

Mentally now, I slapped my wrist as I remembered how apologetic I'd been when I rang the Easy-Clean Staff Agency.

"I — I've always been better with figures, you see . . . I've a demanding job, and — well — I wondered if you could send me someone — say twice a week . . .?"

The lady who had answered the telephone sounded as if she was really dealing in top-class fashion models instead of char ladies. And her prices matched.

"I'm sure you'll be more than satisfied, madam," she said, when we'd finalised the arrangements. "Say Mondays and Fridays, mid-morning?"

"Great!" I'd said, automatically assigning Mondays for clearing up after the weekend — and Fridays to prepare for the next one.

Not that much seemed to be happening on my weekends lately, since my last boyfriend Andy and I had split up.

"I'll be looking forward to the transformation . . ."

TRANSFORMATION was certainly the word, I thought on Friday night when I came home laden with shopping and papers from work. The living-room was positively pristine! Even the coffee mug I'd left had gone — all traces of its mark wiped from the telephone table.

A "DAILY" WITH A DIFFERENCE

Again, I took off my shoes and padded into the bedroom, preparing to transform the workaday me to the weekend, relaxing me, all over again.

And immediately, I saw the second note, propped up grimly against the dressing-table mirror.

Miss Harley, it began tersely, I really must ask you to keep your bedroom tidier. I am not a slave, and I have only two hours here. Thank you, L. Pedford.

"Of all the cheek!" I said aloud. Deliberately, I took my suit off, and dropped it on the floor. Then, I picked up the note again, and sat down, frowning, on the bed.

For the first time, I tried to imagine what this Pedford woman was like. Possibly aged 30 to 35 — maybe with children, and a husband who was most probably out of work.

Those words "I am not a slave" did it, I think. I got up, picked the suit off the floor, and hung it carefully in the wardrobe.

Over the weekend, which once again seemed to drag, I found myself thinking of my charlady quite a lot. I thought of what Sonia had said, about everybody doing what they were good at.

She, Ms Pedford (I refused to think of her as Mrs, just in case) was good at cleaning. Of that there was no doubt. But she obviously resented having to do it for a living.

Sadly I thought of her, as I lay in bed on Sunday night, imagining a younger version of Hilda Ogden scurrying round picking up my tights after me and making me feel guilty, and maybe, gradually becoming aware that in different circumstances, she could have been something like a chartered accountant, too.

On Monday morning before I rushed off to work, I scribbled a note on the telephone pad. L.P. Sorry about the bedroom. Will be more careful in future. I know you're not a slave. Glad you know it, too!

Yours sincerely,

V. Harley.

At lunchtime, I met Sonia, and found myself telling her about my char. "She sounds as if she could be really good for the Women-Unite Group," she said, sounding impressed. "You know — really militant and oppressed . . ."

"No," I said, shaking my head thoughtfully, imagining the Hilda Ogden figure again. "She's just making a small point, I think. I probably won't get any more communications . . ."

But when I got home that night, there was a huge note pinned over the mantelpiece in the living-room. In red, felt-tip pen (mine!), it said,

Bedroom better. But kitchen a shambles! Have you been feeding elephants in there?

"Well!" Shaking with anger, I picked up the telephone. I was going to tell Ms Pedford once and for all! Next-door's Dalmatian might have been a bit muddy when he came in for supper but that was no reason for her to have a nervous breakdown about it!

A "DAILY" WITH A DIFFERENCE

And it wasn't my fault if she wasn't being "stretched" enough, and had to resort to menial tasks, just because she was female!

The woman at the agency was the same as before — cool and collected, and, I imagined, impeccably turned out. After we'd chatted about the weather, I said, "This cleaner you've sent me — called Pedford?"

There was a pause at the other end of the line, then, "Yes? I say — there are no complaints, I hope, Miss Harley?"

Now, I paused. Again, I thought of the woman — the kids — the out-of-work husband.

What had she done, anyway, but complain about my total untidiness? It was only what my mother had been doing for years!

"Oh, it — it'll be all right," I said quickly. "I'll deal with it myself. I have a day off due to me. I'll take it on Friday and wait in . . ."

Surely somebody with a framed certificate to say what she was — to say nothing of a string of A and O-levels — somebody who was used to dealing with personnel into the bargain — shouldn't be worried about having to tell a charlady one or two home truths, I thought.

O N Friday morning I was in the flat thinking I really shouldn't have taken the time off. It only made the weekend longer . . . I sat down and thought about changing my life — it was time I made more of an effort. After all, Andy and I had been finished for quite a few weeks now, and the split hadn't exactly been traumatic.

Maybe, I pondered, I should take up some new interest — like painting, or yoga.

I was still sitting there when the front door opened, and I heard someone walk into the hall.

"Hello! It's all right," I called at the glass partition. "I'm not at work today . . ."

"So there won't be any need for me to write a note . . .?" an alarmingly deep voice answered. And to my amazement, a tall, dark-haired, incredibly dishy man walked in!

Immediately, thoughts of intruders raced through my mind. "Who are you?" I demanded, jumping up. "And how did you get in? The agency said only Mrs Pedford would be given the key . . ."

As he frowned across at me, I

121

A "DAILY" WITH A DIFFERENCE

imagined the difficult Mrs Pedford turning out to be the leader of a criminal gang who specialised in having duplicate keys cut and getting into houses while their owners were out.

To my astonishment, he threw back his head and laughed — a pleasant sound that reverberated right through me.

"There's no Mrs Pedford, unless you count my mother in Wales," he said. "I'm Leo Pedford, your cleaner!"

"B-but!" I couldn't believe it. I took a step back. "I thought . . ."

"I know . . . I gathered that from the 'slave' note," he replied, grinning. "You thought I was some poor little exploited female, instead of just an out-of-work actor who enjoys housework."

"Enjoys . . .?" I could believe that even less. He looked at me as Sonia used to, when she told me she'd always wanted to be a motor mechanic. "But how can you . . . I mean . . .? Are you really an actor? Why . . .?"

He picked up my breakfast coffee mug, and frowned at the ring underneath it.

"Of course I'm an actor. I'm just waiting for my agent to find me something new. But cleaning is so therapeutic — no thinking or learning necessary, just straightforward light, manual work.

"I agree it's not easy to enjoy it here," he went on grumpily, "with one room always looking like a tip — but it is possible to get a real, creative buzz out of restoring order from chaos — making wood and glass shine, and so on.

"Men can be just as good at that as women — once you forget your prejudices . . ."

"Prejudice!" I stared at him indignantly. He really was super, I thought through my annoyance, and as our eyes met, I noticed a twinkle in his eye that told me he didn't find me unattractive either.

"I'm not prejudiced . . .!" I began hotly. It was the first time in my life I had ever been accused of that, and I wondered what Sonia and the others at the Women-Unite Group would have said.

Leo Pedford came closer, and I could see the green flecks in his hazel eyes.

"Oh, no?" he challenged. "Well, how come you took it for granted I was a Ms and not a Mr? How come you assumed I wasn't what I am — a man who needs a job and happens to like cleaning?"

Chastened, I swallowed. "I must admit," I said, thinking of Hilda Ogden again. "I did jump to conclusions . . ."

Going to the cupboard, he took out the vacuum cleaner, as if he'd done it more than just those few times before, and would definitely be doing it for a long time to come.

"Well how about having dinner with me tonight to make amends, Victoria Harley?" he asked, smiling. "And I'll give you a few hints on being useful as well as brainy and beautiful!"

"That," I murmured, as our eyes met again, "is an offer I definitely can't refuse!" □

Complete Story by JOY
MARY HIGHAM

"CONGRATULATIONS TO ME!"

**It hurt to have to say it herself — but obviously
no-one else in the family was going to wish her
Happy Birthday!**

WAKING, I lay for a moment, while reality broke through my
dreams. Not that I welcomed reality. It was too harsh. For
wasn't it Monday? And wasn't Paul still in San Francisco? And
yes, it was my birthday! I was twenty-nine!

Groaning, I snuggled back into the warm. What I'd really like to do
was just stay in bed . . . But life did have to go on, didn't it?

Wearily I pushed aside the covers.

"Come on, kids! Time to get up!" I shouted.

Of course, they might remember it's my birthday, I thought, pulling
back the curtains to reveal a grey, drizzly morning. Miracles had been
known to happen . . .

Better not to expect too much, though. After all, Monday — and a wet
Monday at that — is so devastating it obliterates everything else.
Especially when you're only children aged seven and eight years.

As I'd expected, the normal chaos of lost socks and dinner money,
unwashed ears, unbrushed hair and bolted breakfasts, absorbed all their

123

"CONGRATULATIONS TO ME!"

mind and energy. All mine, too, until I heard the postman delivering letters.

Dashing into the hall, I shuffled them. A card from Dad — that'd have a cheque inside; one from Auntie Clare; one from Briony — bless her, she always remembered; one from Paul's parents . . . But nothing with an American stamp.

Oh, darling, how could you have forgotten? Blinking back the tears, I returned to the kitchen. Now it was gumboots that were lost. And what about that button missing on Karen's raincoat?

"You said you'd sew it on, Mummy, and you forgot!"

I bit my lip. "I'm sorry, love. I'll do it tonight. I promise."

She frowned. "Don't suppose it'll be raining tonight."

Grabbing Juliet's hand, I slammed the door shut behind us. We were, as always, late.

As always, we scurried down the road and, as always, I shooed them through the school gates just in time.

Justin's mum heard my deep sigh.

She grinned. "It's a grim day, isn't it, Sally?"

"It's worse than that," I told her as we started back. "It's my birthday. I'm twenty-nine. Next year's the point of no return —"

"Next year?" She laughed. "Lucky old you! I passed that centuries ago!" Then, reading my rueful face: "Paul still away?"

I nodded, hands clenched inside the pockets of my anorak.

"Come round to my place — have a coffee," she urged. "I haven't a proper cake, but there's some of yesterday's Dundee left. We could pretend."

"Oh, Carol, that's awfully sweet of you," I cried, genuinely touched. "But — well, I don't want to leave the house for long, Paul's sure to ring."

"Of course." She understood. "You hurry home, then. I'm going round by the shops."

But home was empty, grubby, untidy, its silence thick as an eiderdown, disturbed only by a neighbour's dog barking and the whoosh of traffic through puddles.

I threw myself down on the only uncluttered chair.

I'd give Paul half an hour. If he hadn't rung by then, I'd make a cup of tea. If, by the time I'd drunk it, he still hadn't rung . . . Well, then I'd better start clearing up.

But he would ring, wouldn't he?

It was gone eleven and I was upstairs dusting when at last the phone bell shrilled.

I ran down two at a time, pulses racing.

"Hello."

"HI, there, Sal. I was making up the spare beds and remembered it was your birthday. Sorry your card'll be late. I didn't get it off till Saturday —"

"Making up the beds?" I queried. "Whatever for?"

"CONGRATULATIONS TO ME!"

But as usual, my sister, Kate, didn't stop for explanations, racing on instead to chat of other things.

TEN minutes later I dropped the receiver back in its cradle, sweating at the thought of Paul trying to get through from the States, only to hear the engaged signal.

Kate had reminded me about cards, though, and opening those made me feel better. Dad's cheque was even more generous than usual. Dear Dad, perhaps he knew I'd be lonesome . . .

That's when a thought came to me. A thought that grew, like a germ, and refused to go away.

If Paul still hadn't rung by the time I collected the children, we'd come back via that little antique shop.

Last time we'd passed there'd been a silver locket in the window. Heart-shaped, it was, and very pretty.

I'd pointed it out to Paul, but he'd been talking to Karen at the time and hadn't noticed. At least, I don't think he had.

Well, if my nearest and dearest weren't going to remember, I'd give myself a present.

So I hedged my bets and waited.

Crispbread, cheese and a yoghurt, then I tackled the mountain of ironing with the radio tuned to "Woman's Hour".

Yet who can concentrate on embroidered pictures and rich brown stews when it's your birthday and the man you love is not only thousands of miles away, but has forgotten?

Oh, how I willed that phone to ring . . .

It didn't, though. And when I left the house for the second time, I was dressed to go to the antique shop after I'd picked up the kids.

I joined the knot of mums at the school gates. Carol smiled. "Heard from Paul then?"

I smiled back. "Not yet," I admitted, relieved as voices and a rush of feet saved me from saying more.

"Cor! Look at all these puddles! Come on, Juliet! Let's see who can make the biggest splashes!"

At the thought of the locket, a tiny glimmer of sunlight illuminated my world.

But it was a glimmer quickly extinguished when we arrived at the shop. For the locket was no longer in the front of the window. Glancing swiftly amongst the massed bric-à-brac, I couldn't see it anywhere.

Already fearing the worst, I shepherded reluctant children inside.

"I know the one you mean," the young man said. "But I'm afraid it's been sold."

I gulped. "I knew it," I said. "And I'd set my heart on that locket."

"I'm sorry. Perhaps there's something else you'd like? We've some lovely cut glass. Beautiful rings — brooches —"

But I didn't want anything else. Sadly, I shook my head. Going home,

"CONGRATULATIONS TO ME!"

Juliet had to tug at my sleeve to make me listen to what she was saying.

BOTH the children were in bed when, at last, the phone rang. Dully I lifted the receiver and recited the number. This wouldn't — it couldn't — be Paul . . .

"Hello, darling! Happy birthday!"

"Ooooh!" It was a long, long sigh. "I — I thought you'd forgotten."

"Forgotten?" Paul's voice was loud, clear and cheerful. "Good grief, what time do you think it is out here?

"I'm still in my pyjamas, I'd have you know. For goodness' sake, I had to wake the girl on the switchboard before she'd put me through!"

And then I remembered. Of course, America was hours behind us in time. And Paul was right over on the Pacific seaboard, so there it'd be even further behind.

"Darling, I'm sorry," I said. "I should never had doubted you."

"You certainly shouldn't," he countered, and I could picture the twinkle in his bright blue eyes. "Especially as I've a present for you."

"A present?" I cried. "What is it?"

"You'll see."

"You mean I shan't know till you come back?"

He laughed. "I didn't say that, did I?"

"But you will be back soon, won't you?"

He laughed again. "Missed me, eh?"

I blinked back tears. "You could say that."

"Perhaps you won't have to wait that long."

"You mean you're coming soon?" I cried.

But he wouldn't be drawn. "I mean, my sweet, that I'd like to speak to the kids. Are they around?"

"Around?" I objected. "They've been in bed and asleep for hours."

"Then you'll have to haul them out. There's something I want to tell them."

"Oh, Paul! Can't it wait till you're home?"

"No. And do hurry, love. This call's costing a bomb."

The children were not, of course, asleep as I'd imagined, but hanging over the banisters. One word, and they tumbled down the stairs like bouncing balls.

"Hi, Dad!" Bright faces were glued to the receiver. "Yes, yes, we know . . . OK, we'll tell her . . . Just like you said . . . All right, Dad, 'Bye!"

Thrusting the phone back on me, they shot away, intent on some private business.

Paul was saying, "I'm sorry it's so late in your day, darling."

"It doesn't matter," I assured him. "Not now."

"And you won't doubt me, ever again?"

"I promise."

"I do love you."

"CONGRATULATIONS TO ME!"

I shut my eyes. The bedroom above my head seemed to have turned into an army parade ground, there was so much bumping and thumping.

"I love you, too, Paul."

"Tell 'em to hurry, though," he begged. "I can't hang on all day."

But already the door had slammed open.

"Happy birthday, Mummy!"

They stood there, without dressing-gowns, bare footed, trousers at half mast, but triumphantly bearing gifts.

Then, as one, they launched themselves, and I was so enmeshed with scrambling, hugging children I almost dropped the phone.

"This one's from me!" Juliet's parcel was thrust under my nose. "Open it, Mummy! Quickly!"

Disengaging arms, I tore at the parcel she handed me. Inside was a crayoned card and an embroidered hankie.

"It's beautiful, darling. Simply beautiful."

She beamed. "Daddy helped me choose it."

I heard a distant laugh. "Good old Daddy!"

"And he promised to ring on the proper day," Karen added. "Only it'd be late. I don't know why — something about the world going round."

"My world's going round anyway," I admitted. "And is this one from you, Karen?"

She nodded eagerly. "It's sweets. A big box. We like sweets, don't we, Juliet?"

"Hey!" Paul chipped in. "What about my present?"

"Yours?" I cried. "Oh, darling, you didn't buy me the locket, after all?"

But the packet the girls put into my hands wasn't locket shaped. It was oblong, and felt soft.

"Whatever is it?" I asked.

Three voices answered me. "Open it! Find out!"

Quickly I peeled away the gift wrapping. Inside was a folder stuffed with documents. And, on the top, an airline ticket to San Francisco.

"Oh, Paul!" I gasped, staring at the package in disbelief.

"You approve? You'll come?"

"Darling — need you ask? Of course I'll come!"

"We're going to have a holiday, too," Juliet crowed. "We're going to Auntie Kate's." And suddenly, Kate's strange comment on the phone about "making up beds . . ." made sense after all.

My eyes misted with tears.

"You knew?" I whispered. "All of you? All the time?"

Paul chuckled. "You don't think I'd plan a surprise like this without telling them, do you?" he cried.

"And we all knew you'd like it better than any silly old locket," Karen added. "But come on, Mummy. Open my parcel. We want one of my sweets."

And what could I do, but oblige? □

To Tell The Truth

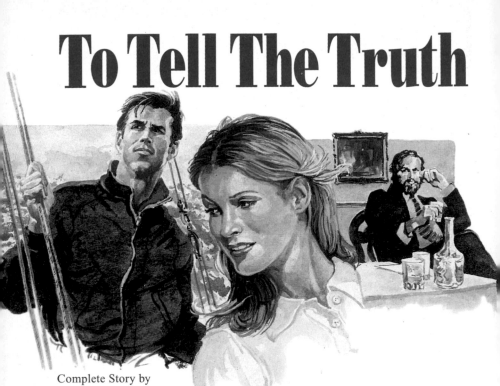

Complete Story by
ISOBEL STEWART

. . . she wasn't the girl he thought she was. But she could hardly tell the man of her dreams that!

FROM the kitchen window, Jenny watched her small daughter playing in the sand-pit with Simon from next door. "Put more sand in the pail — you haven't got enough," Simon ordered imperiously, with all the authority of a six-year-old male to a four-year-old female.

"Yeth, Thimon," Kim said obediently.

Oh, Kim, Jenny thought, between love and exasperation, you must learn to stand up for yourself. Don't be a doormat!

And the words seemed to echo round the room, taking her back over the years . . .

* * * *

"Don't be a doormat, Jenny," Richard said, his voice sharp with irritation.

She looked at him, surprised, and he coloured.

"I'm sorry," he apologised, a little stiffly. "I had no right to say that.

But — Jenny, I just asked you what you had done at the weekend, and you said you went sailing. You went sailing last weekend, too, and the one before that.

"Now, you and I have been working together for over a year, and somehow I've never thought of you as being mad about outdoor activities. Suddenly, you're very fond of sailing. Or — are you, Jenny?"

"No," Jenny replied, honestly. "I don't really like sailing much at all, but Charles does."

Richard looked at her, thoughtfully, and for no good reason she felt herself redden. Being his personal assistant did not give him the right to comment on her private life.

"It's good for me, getting fresh air after being shut up in the office all week," she pointed out quickly.

"Of course it is," Richard agreed. "And I'm sure the fresh air on the golf course and up in the mountains did you a great deal of good, too, when Charles was keen on golf and climbing."

They had reached the block of flats where Jenny lived, and fond as she was of Richard, she was relieved. But he wasn't giving up that easily.

"We haven't discussed the new office system," he reminded her.

Jenny gave in, although she knew very well it wasn't the new office system they would be discussing.

"Well, come up and have some coffee," she offered.

While she was setting out the coffee mugs, and laying out some of the biscuits her mother had sent a few days ago, Richard sat at the tiny table and gave his opinion on the new office system.

But by the time she sat beside him, the system was dealt with and there was no escaping the determination in Richard's blue eyes.

"I know," he said quietly, "it's none of my business, but you and I have been friends for quite a while, Jenny, haven't we? Our friendship means a great deal to me."

"To me, too," Jenny told him, meaning it. It was a friendship that had developed slowly, easily, naturally, as they discussed their work together and the business in general. At one time, Jenny had thought that perhaps, in time . . .

But she had met Charles, and from that moment, there was no question of anyone else, ever.

"Has he asked you to marry him?" Richard asked.

"Not yet," she replied, not meaning to sound defensive, but knowing that she had. "We've only known each other for eight months, Richard. There — there's plenty time."

"If I was Charles," Richard said quietly, "I wouldn't risk having a girl like you and not making absolutely sure everyone knew she was mine."

For a moment, his eyes said a great deal more than his words. But there was nothing Jenny could say, for how, she wondered, can you apologise to a man for falling in love with someone else, and not him? So she sat silent, an ache in her throat.

TO TELL THE TRUTH

Then Richard leaned across the little table, and smiled.

"It's all right, Jenny," he told her. "We'll always be good friends."

There was nothing cynical or sarcastic in his voice, and a wave of affection for him filled her.

"Charles hasn't looked at another girl since we met," Jenny pointed out, not quite steadily.

"Charles doesn't want a girl, he wants a doormat," he returned. "And anyway, how much time or energy can he have left after all this activity out on the river?"

Richard drained his coffee cup.

"What you have to do, Jenny," he told her decisively, "is to assert yourself. Make him see right now that he must have some consideration for you. Otherwise — what kind of a life are you going to have? Do you want to spend the rest of your life sailing, or climbing, or whatever this guy feels he wants to do?"

He took a folded piece of paper from his pocket, and put it on the table.

"I looked out some of my old psychology notes from university on assertive rights — have a read of them, see what you think."

He stood up.

"Thanks for the coffee, Jenny — we'll fix up the installation of the new office equipment tomorrow." At the door, he turned.

"Charles knows you and I walk home together most days, and I often come in like this?" he asked her.

"Of course he does," Jenny replied, once again defensive. "You know that."

"And he doesn't mind?" Richard asked. He shook his head. "He's pretty sure of himself and — pretty sure of you."

The door closed behind him, and Jenny sat down. Her coffee was cold, so she poured herself another cup, then, a little unwillingly, she opened the paper Richard had given her, and read through his notes.

By standing up for our rights we show we respect ourselves and achieve respect from others, she read.

But Charles respects me, she told herself quickly, so that doesn't apply.

Sacrificing our rights usually results in destroying relationships.

Destroying relationships? Because the relationship was built on something untrue, insecure — like her letting Charles believe she enjoyed sailing, when, in fact, she dreaded the motion of the tiny yacht. Jenny hated being cold and wet, and it was only by not eating before she went out, that she managed not to be sea-sick.

Slowly, she read on.

If we don't tell people how their behaviour negatively affects us, we are denying them an opportunity to change their behaviour.

But that's right, she thought, surprised. If I don't let Charles know that I don't like sailing, how can I expect him to understand?

When we are assertive, everyone involved usually benefits.

Jenny folded up the paper.

I will be assertive, she told herself. I will stand up for my rights. I will tell Charles that I don't enjoy sailing. I will insist that if I'm prepared to do some of the things he enjoys, he should also be prepared to do some of the things I enjoy.

JENNY stood up, took the coffee cups to the sink and washed them. And then, with the drying-up cloth in her hand, she stopped. I don't want to spend every weekend for the rest of my life sailing, she thought, but I do want to spend the rest of my life with Charles. And maybe if I'm not prepared to do the things he wants I won't have the chance to do that. Perhaps Richard is right. Charles does want a doormat, not a girl.

Suddenly, inside her, a little voice — very assertive, she realised later — asked her — wouldn't you rather be Charles' doormat than anyone else's girl?

I'd rather be his girl with no question of a doormat, she returned, just as assertively.

She looked at the clock. She'd have to hurry to finish that dusting before Charles came to pick her up to watch him playing squash.

Wait a minute, Jenny told herself. Wait a minute. She took a deep breath. It didn't do as much as she had hoped it would, so she took another.

And then, deliberately, she turned away from the housework. It was a lovely day, and it was ages since she had sat — just sat — out on her balcony, with her face lifted to the unusually warm October sun.

Determinedly, Jenny sat in the sun and relaxed.

She was still relaxing when she heard Charles' familiar knock on the door, and she forced herself to go right on relaxing, and to call to him. But something went wrong between her head and her feet, and she found herself standing up and going to him when he came out of the little hallway.

"Hi, Jen," he said, and he took her in his arms and kissed her. And once again the ground beneath her feet became Cloud Nine.

"Hi," she said at last, when he released her.

"Finished your housework?" Charles asked briskly. "Right, let's be off, the court is booked, I don't want to be late."

Assert yourself, Jenny reminded herself.

"Looks as if the weather is all set for the weekend," Charles remarked, picking up the newspaper. "We should get a good breeze out on the river."

Instantly, Jenny could feel the cold and the wet, and the uneasiness inside her, and asserting herself didn't seem such a bad idea.

"You go to squash, Charles," she told him. "I haven't done my housework, so I'll get it done while you play. Come back here when you finish, and we'll have something to eat if you like."

He looked down at her, his dark eyes clouded.

TO TELL THE TRUTH

"I'd much rather you came, too, Jen," he said.

Jenny hardened her heart.

"Enjoy your game," she told him briskly, "I should be finished here by the time you get back."

But she hadn't quite finished when he came back, so he told her to go on, and he would make something for them to eat.

Ten minutes later Jenny went through to her kitchen and found him with one of her frilly aprons tied round him, breaking eggs into a bowl. His dark, unruly hair was still damp from his shower after the game. He looked, she thought, like one of the little boys in her class, as he concentrated on whisking the eggs.

"Why don't these eggs look frothy like they do when you whisk them?" he asked, turning to her.

"Because you're using the whisk like a cement mixer," she told him. "Do it lightly."

"I'm an engineer, not a chef," Charles pointed out.

Somehow, Jenny found herself with the bowl in her hands, and the apron tied around her, and Charles was sitting at the table telling her about his game. The omelette was light and fluffy, and Charles was suitably appreciative.

Later they sat on the couch, and the TV programme wasn't really worth watching, so they didn't watch it, and Jenny thought that she was more interested in just being with Charles, being his girl, than being assertive.

But the next day, Richard asked her if she was going sailing that weekend, and she told him, no, she wasn't. And that night, she told Charles the same thing.

"What do you mean, not coming sailing?" he asked her, unbelieving. "I told you, the weather's going to be perfect. It was much too calm last time."

Too calm? Jenny shuddered, remembering.

"There's ballet on TV at night. I want to see it," she told him.

He looked down at her. She knew he didn't enjoy ballet, he'd told her.

"We could be back in plenty time for the ballet," he offered.

She hadn't expected this. But she reminded herself, quickly, that that didn't really change anything. She was still sacrificing her rights — and one of her rights was not to enjoy sailing.

"Charles," she said, clearly, "I don't really like sailing."

He looked at her, astounded.

"You don't like sailing?" he repeated.

Having said it once, made it easier to say again, Jenny found.

"I don't like sailing," she repeated.

"Why didn't you say so, then?" he asked, reasonably.

Jenny looked away.

"Because you like it," she replied, her voice low. There was silence — a long silence.

"I appreciate that, Jen," Charles said, carefully, "but I'd much rather

132

TO TELL THE TRUTH

you had been honest with me."

Jenny swallowed.

"I thought I might grow to like it," she told him. And then, brightly — "Well, I'm being honest now. You enjoy your sailing, with your good stiff breeze, and when you get back, come up and — join me in watching ballet, if you like."

He said he would do that, but if she changed her mind, about sailing, just to ring him.

Jenny said — very positively, very assertively — that she wasn't likely to. And when Saturday came she pottered around her little flat doing all the things she used to do on Saturdays in pre-Charles days.

Jenny sat out on her balcony to have lunch, and she told herself that this was much more her kind of Saturday.

In the afternoon, she went for a walk, and from a high point she could see the bay, with the bright sails scudding over the blue water. Charles must be enjoying his sailing today, she told herself, and she reminded herself that although it looked lovely from up here, down there she would be wet, cold and miserable.

Then she went back home and washed her hair, and put a casserole in the oven, hoping it would behave as it should, and be ready when it was needed.

Charles arrived just before the ballet started, a little breathless, but not too breathless to kiss her thoroughly. After that Jenny was breathless, too, and together they carried trays through with supper for both of them, and switched on the television.

The casserole, he told her, was delicious, and she had to admit he was right.

The ballet was just as good as she had hoped it would be, and Charles made one or two reasonably interested comments. When it was finished, she asked him how his sailing had been, and he told her. It took a good half-hour.

Then he switched off the TV and said he didn't think there would be anything more worth watching, and Jenny said she'd make some coffee, but he told her he didn't want coffee, not right now.

Charles took her in his arms and, with his lips on hers, Jenny forgot about sailing, about ballet, about being assertive, about everything but being in his arms, and wanting to stay there for the rest of her life.

I WAS very assertive at the weekend," she told Richard on Monday, when they were sharing their coffee-break. "I told Charles I didn't like sailing, and I said I wanted to watch ballet, and it worked. He went sailing, and then he watched ballet with me.

"And I'm not going to sit and watch him playing squash, he can come and see me when he finishes playing."

Richard put his coffee mug down.

"I'm glad it seems to be working out," he said, and he smiled. But

133

there was something in his smile that made Jenny feel uncomfortable.

That weekend, when Charles came back from sailing, he took her to a new little Italian restaurant for supper, and then to see a film they had been waiting for. The weekend after that he was away doing a two-day nature-trail hike.

"It was arranged ages ago," he said, not apologising, Jenny realised, just telling her. "I had your name down for it as well, but I realise now I shouldn't have done that without asking you if you wanted to come."

"Thank you, Charles," Jenny replied, a little bewildered by the immediate success she was having by being assertive, by standing up for her rights.

"You'll be all right, will you?" he asked, and she assured him that she would be. There was some dressmaking she wanted to do, she said, and one of the office typists had been asking her to go for tea, and then she had letters to write.

"Fine," Charles said, a little strangely, she thought. "I'll give you a ring when I get back."

"Do," Jenny replied, cheerfully. "And enjoy your hike, Charles."

The weekend was pleasant and restful. Jenny did all the things she wanted to do, and when she saw the pile of letters waiting to be posted,

she could actually feel the glow of virtue.

Not only had she written an extra-long letter to her parents on the farm, she had also written to her sister, to her cousin, to two aunts and three old schoolfriends.

It would be late on Sunday evening when Charles returned, and although she hoped he would phone her, she wasn't counting on it. But at seven o'clock her doorbell rang.

He was still in his hiking clothes, and he hadn't shaved, and when he stood there, looking down at her, her heart thudded so unsteadily that she could hardly hear what he was saying.

". . . back early, so I came right here. Can I come in?" he said.

Jenny only realised that she was holding the door half-closed. Without a word, she opened it, and he followed her in.

"I'm sorry," he said, formally, "my boots are dirty." And then, before she could either accept or refuse his apology, he gripped her arms.

"Jenny, all the time I was away, I kept thinking. About you. About us. You've no idea how it shook me to find out that you haven't really liked so many of the things we've done together, but I don't think that really matters. I want to know that when I come home you'll be here, always."

His hands tightened on her arms.

"What are you saying, Charles?" she asked, because she had to hear him say it.

"I'm asking you to marry me, of course, Jen," he said, surprised.

She didn't know whether to laugh or cry, but before she could do either, he kissed her.

Later — much later — Jenny moved her head from its very comfortable position on his shoulder.

"Charles," she said, drowsily, "if I hadn't started asserting myself —"

"Oh, is that what you were doing?" he asked, and she could hear without looking at him that he was smiling.

"If I hadn't," she went on, "would you have asked me to marry you?"

"Oh yes," he replied immediately, and her heart lifted. And then he went on, cheerfully and honestly, "sooner or later."

"Sooner or later," Jenny repeated aloud. And suddenly, the words and the way he had said them seemed to pin-point his whole attitude to her.

"Sooner or later, indeed!" she said to him furiously. "Well, let me tell you, Charles Hamilton, that isn't good enough. Ever since I met you, you've treated me like a — like a doormat! We've done what you wanted to do, we've gone where you wanted to go, we've eaten what you've wanted to eat.

"And if Richard hadn't told me I should assert myself, that's what we'd still be doing. And — and it isn't good enough! So you can —"

Charles was standing very still, and for a moment she was at a loss for words. But only for a moment. "So you can take your dirty hiking boots off my carpet and out of my life!"

"If that's what you want," Charles said coldly, "I'll go."

Without another word, he turned and walked out. Jenny stared at the muddy track he had left, and even when the door closed, firmly, finally, she didn't move.

Only when she heard his footsteps going down the stairs, did she go through to the kitchen for a brush and a dustpan. When the carpet was clean again, she put the brush and pan into the cupboard, carefully.

To her surprise, she saw that it was still only five past seven. I'll go and see Richard, she decided, and tell him — tell him he was right, and I'm finished with Charles.

RICHARD was delighted and surprised to see her. He set aside the work he had been doing and listened carefully while she told him. "So it's finished?" he said at last.

Treacherously, her heart lurched.

TO TELL THE TRUTH

"Yes, it's finished," she told him firmly.

He took both her hands in his.

"I don't think I need to tell you how I feel about you, Jenny," he said, quietly, and he kissed her. They drew apart, and she looked at him, and the disappointment in his eyes made her ache.

"Richard," she said, quickly, "it's too soon — give me time. Perhaps later —"

He shook his head.

"No, Jenny," he told her. "It would be second-best, and that isn't good enough for either of us." He stood up, and patted her shoulder. "Go on home, Jenny, and — think about things."

He kissed her cheek lightly, a friendly kiss, and then he said he'd walk up the street with her. But he left her at the entrance to her own flat, and there was something very final, Jenny realised, in the way he said goodbye. Just as there was something very final about the silence of her own flat, and the cleanness of the newly-brushed carpet. Something frighteningly final.

Jenny was still standing there, when her doorbell rang. Richard, she told herself, as she turned and went to open the door. He's decided not to leave me alone right now, he's realised I need company.

But it wasn't Richard, it was Charles. He had changed, and his hair was roughly towelled dry.

"My shoes are clean," he said abruptly, and she saw that he was very angry. "May I come in?"

Silently, she held the door open.

"If I treated you like a doormat," he told her, as if he was carrying on a conversation of a moment ago, "it was because you let me. You weren't being fair to yourself or to me, not being honest with me. You weren't giving us a fair chance.

"How could I know you hated all these things if you didn't tell me? It was downright selfish, not letting me know how you felt!"

Jenny said nothing. There was nothing to say, she knew, because it was true.

"And what's more," Charles went on, "in all this talk of doormats and being assertive, you forgot something, and so did I."

"What did I forget?" Jenny asked, not quite steadily, more shaken than she would have thought possible, by seeing him like this.

He looked down at her, unsmiling.

"You forgot that I love you," he said loudly, angrily.

He kissed her then, a kiss that started off angrily, aggressively, but somehow changed midway into a kiss unlike any kiss Jenny had known before.

"And that changes everything," Charles murmured, at last, his lips still close to hers.

"What changes what?" Jenny asked, bemused.

"Me loving you, and you loving me," he told her. "We can work out everything else, because of that. You don't have to come sailing, and I don't have to watch ballet, but once in a while we might both try them out again, just in case. Let's keep our options open, right?"

"Right," Jenny agreed.

She found, a little to her surprise, that they were sitting on the couch now, and his arm was around her.

"We'll get married just as soon as possible," he was saying now. "No fuss, no nonsense, there's no point in wasting time, and my flat will do for the moment, but we can look for a bigger one. Tomorrow I'll —"

"Wait a minute," Jenny said, clearly.

He waited, his dark brows drawn together.

"I want a wedding with fuss and nonsense," she told him, but she smiled as she said it. "I want to be married in the little church in the village at home, and I want to wear a white dress and a veil.

"I want all my folk there, even my Great-Aunt Aggie, and she always cries at weddings, and I want all your folk there. Flowers in the church, and afterwards we'll walk up the village street, and —"

"All right," Charles said hastily, "I get the picture." He was smiling, too. "I think you've made your feelings clear. We'll have a white wedding."

It wouldn't, Jenny knew, be the end of it. There would be times when she would think he was bossy, domineering, arrogant. Times when he would think she was being selfish, and not entirely honest. But — he was right, what really mattered was this, loving each other, and wanting to spend the rest of their lives together.

* * * *

Slowly, yesterday became today, and Jenny was back in her sunny kitchen, listening for the baby to wake up, and watching her daughter playing outside.

As she watched, Simon lifted a bucket of sand and poured it over Kim, from head to foot, slowly, methodically. Kim stood perfectly still.

Don't be a doormat, Jenny said to her small daughter, silently, forcing herself not to run out straight away, forcing herself to give Kim a chance.

"No, Thimon," Kim said sweetly. "I thaid not to do that."

She bent down and filled the bucket again, and this time she emptied it over Simon.

And Jenny, watching the two sand-covered children eyeing each other consideringly, knew that she needn't have worried about her daughter being a doormat.

Tonight, she thought, smiling, I must tell Charles. He'll enjoy that. And on Sunday, when we go to Richard and Ellen for the baby's christening, I'll tell Richard. He'll enjoy it, too.

Still smiling, Jenny went out to clean up the children. □

The Best Of The Bargains

That's what he had been getting at every auction — outbidding her! No wonder she was so keen to see him going, going — gone!

I'LL take ten pounds! Thank you, madam . . . twenty, sir . . .? The bidding's with you, madam . . . twenty . . .? five . . . ? thirty, sir?" Deborah felt the auctioneer's eyes rest questioningly on hers again. She gave a slow shake of her head and a small sigh. The piece was worth £10 — certainly no more.

Whoever was bidding would have difficulty making a profit when they sold it again.

She glanced behind to see who the reckless spender was. Annoyance crossed her features when she recognised the same young man who had been at the sale at Barleycross.

He caught her gaze at the identical moment and gave a shrug, mouthing the word, "sorry." She felt her annoyance mount. It wasn't she who deserved pity — it was him.

She saw his expression change to a friendly smile and flushed angrily. Tossing her auburn hair, she faced the front again.

The auctioneer was announcing the next piece. It was one she had marked on her programme with an extra sharp tick. In her small antique shop called Merry Meeting she had a good sale for delicate Victorian furniture.

The piece she had examined before the sale was one of the finest escritoires she had seen. In her mind she had already linked it with a certain buyer.

If she could purchase it at the right price she would have an instant sale as soon as she returned home. Mrs Hughes, one of her regulars, was bound to be interested.

When the bargaining began, she remained silent until some of the other dealers had dropped out. Then she made a signal to the auctioneer to show her interest.

Her price was raised from someone behind her. Deborah turned sharply. The bidding was once again between her and the young man.

Petulance made her bring the price up to almost as much as she could afford. Still the young man bettered it.

THE BEST OF THE BARGAINS

plete Story By
LLA ROSS

139

THE BEST OF THE BARGAINS

Quandary set in as the auctioneer's eyes rested on hers again.

She risked another £10. Maybe the piece was worth it. The young man bettered it immediately.

Fury goaded her. She wouldn't let him have it! At Barleycross he had stolen all the pieces she'd been interested in. And he'd already outbid her for the last item she'd wanted.

Pique made her raise the price ridiculously. Now — better that, she thought grimly.

Unless the young man had, like her, another Mrs Hughes ready to take it, he'd have the piece on his hands for life.

Then, incredibly, he raised her.

Deborah swallowed. She'd be an idiot to go higher. Slowly she shook her head at the auctioneer. He snapped his hammer on the desk.

"Sold to Mr Faulds for two hundred and seventy pounds!"

Deborah folded her programme, trying to keep anger showing from her movements.

The sale was almost over so she left before the end, sweeping past the young man at the back of the hall.

It was as she was unlocking the door of her blue estate car that she heard a voice from behind and turned. It was the same young man.

He spoke with an embarrassed tone.

"Look — I could see you were disappointed. If the desk means so much to you I'm quite prepared to let you have it for the price you wanted.

"What I mean is — I've bought a lot of other things — one desk here or there isn't going to make much difference . . ."

Indignation overcame her. She replied in scathing terms.

"I wouldn't dream of depriving you of your items. You bought them fair and square. If I'd thought the escritoire worth more I'd have raised you. As it is, I'm quite sure you've paid too much."

She watched his face fall. She had no intention of lingering over a discussion.

Wrenching open the car door, she got in quickly, reversed recklessly, and narrowly missed hitting the saleroom wall.

As she drove down the street of the market town she glanced in her driving mirror to see the young man staring after her.

She focused her eyes on the road ahead, curbing her speed and trying to push him from her mind.

Blast the man! She rarely let temper get the better of her. But his smarmy condescension had really been the last straw.

WHEN she reached the small, attractive shop in the nearby village, her younger sister opened the front door and came out to greet her.

"You're home early! Did the sale finish early? Come and have a cup of coffee. I'll help you unpack the car after."

"I didn't buy anything, I'm afraid."

Bunny's voice was incredulous. "But you usually bring home a car-load from Scottislow!"

"I know!" Deborah found herself snapping. "But prices are high. There was a stupid young man bidding foolishly and everything I wanted he seemed to be after." She went into the kitchen.

Bunny followed. It was easy to see Deborah was upset. That was unusual. Normally her older sister's nature was sunny.

Deborah had looked after her like a mother for the past 10 years, financing Bunny through private school, and building the antique business their father had left them into a successful, paying concern.

Bunny tried to change the subject as they drank their coffee.

THE BEST OF THE BARGAINS

"Did you know old Charlie Allsorts has been taken ill? Apparently he collapsed in his shop last week. They've taken him into hospital."

"No — I didn't know that." Deborah's brow creased. "What's happened to his business? Is anyone else running it?"

"Not that I know of. According to Mrs Hughes, it's been run down for a long time. It was half empty when she last went there. I should think he'll probably put it up for sale."

Conscience attacked Deborah. It had been old Charlie, with his antiques shop called Allsorts in the next village, who had been a tower of strength to her when she'd suddenly been thrust in at the deep end after their father's death.

Most of the other dealers had been either too busy or too jealous of their own concerns to offer her any tips.

But Charlie had introduced her to the world of buying and selling and she had grown very fond of him. He was a wonderful old character and very generous with his time.

"I'll have to visit him," she murmured. "I'll ring and ask about visiting times. I feel awful that I didn't know anything about this before."

When she phoned the hospital she was told that Charlie had been discharged.

"He was feeling much better," the sister told her. "A relative came and took him away. He did leave an address, in case anyone like yourself tried to contact him. I can give it to you if you like?"

Deborah thanked her and wrote the address down. Shropshire was too far away to visit him. But she could always send a card, hoping he'd get well and be home soon.

TWO days later she left Bunny in charge of the shop and drove to a sale 10 miles away in Penbury. As she drove along the country road she pictured the things that were likely to be in the sale.

The once-monthly one was usually a good one. The agents who ran it generally collected some fine pieces. Most of the dealers she knew by sight would probably be there, but there was always enough for all of them.

She parked her car in the nearest car park to the saleroom. The sun was shining and she hummed a snatch of a song she'd heard earlier on the radio, as she made her way towards the double doors.

There were about a dozen people already in the hall. She mingled with them, studying the goods for sale.

Her spirits soared. A lot of the stuff was just what she needed: good china and small furniture. That was perfect for a quick turnover. And there was enough bric-a-brac to satisfy passing trade. And even a delectable Victorian pedestal table to gladden Mrs Hughes' heart.

A woman's voice beside her whispered conspiratorially:

"It's a good one today!"

Deborah looked up from her programme, which she was marking with the usual ticks, to see Amanda Heering smiling at her. The smart, grey-haired woman was the owner of a very good shop in the centre of Barleycross.

Deborah nodded with a hint of reticence.

Amanda noticed and gave a laugh.

"It's all right, my dear. I'm not here to push up the bargains. I know what suits you and I know what suits me."

Deborah hid her programme behind her back.

The woman laughed again and added in a whisper, "I'll tell you what — if you turn a blind eye to the rather nice brasswork in the far corner — I'll be happy to let you bid for the pedestal table without me butting in."

Deborah relaxed.

"It's a deal." She smiled. "But I'm afraid neither of us will get all the things we want." She looked around. "It seems too many people have now heard of the

THE BEST OF THE BARGAINS

Penbury monthly. There seems to be even more of a crowd here than usual."

"Amateurs mainly," Amanda said wryly. "They've probably come out of curiosity. The weather's being too kind." She glanced at her watch.

"There's still twenty minutes to go till the off. Come along and I'll treat you to a cup of coffee."

In the café over the road they met several other dealers who haunted the auctions.

"What's happened to old Charlie Allsorts?" Amanda asked her. "He's usually here with the rest of us. I can't say I've seen him at any of the sales recently."

Deborah told her about his illness.

"Poor old man!" Amanda sympathised. "He's really getting too old to be working. He must be almost eighty. I wonder what'll happen to his business if he has to retire?"

Deborah shook her head. "According to my sister, it's already very run down. I feel guilty that I haven't been to see him for so long."

Amanda gave a sigh. "We all have our own businesses to consider, my dear. This is a cut-throat game. With old Charlie out of the running there'll be a little more trade for the rest of us."

Deborah flinched at her words.

When they went back to the saleroom she was still thinking of Amanda's words. She hated the idea that she was becoming like some of the hardened business men and women that she knew.

If her father had still been alive she doubted whether she would ever have entered the antiques business. In her early teens she had thought about becoming a teacher.

But, after his death, that had been out of the question. She'd had Bunny to consider. It had been a long, uphill struggle to get where she was today at still only 27.

She pushed the thoughts aside as the auctioneer entered the hall. Suddenly she felt Amanda tug her sleeve.

"Look behind you — in the right-hand corner. Do you happen to know that young man? He's been a pain in the neck at all the sales I've attended lately. I have this feeling he's in the American market. He bids crazily for stuff that doesn't fetch more than a few pounds normally."

Deborah turned. The attractive young man, head and shoulders above the elderly dealers close to him, was the same person she'd seen at her two former auctions. Her heart dropped.

He saw her and gave a small wave.

THE BEST OF THE BARGAINS

She felt herself flushing. Ignoring him, she faced the front again.

A cloud of gloom seemed to pass overhead. She found her spirits dropping. He would push up the price of everything she'd marked on her programme. It would mean probably going home with nothing again.

Amanda was regarding her with a raised eyebrow.

"Yes — I've met him before," Deborah hissed. "I agree with you. He's an absolute pain in the neck."

The auctioneer brought the crowd in the hall to order. The buzz of conversation was stilled. He cracked a few short jokes. And then the sale began.

As Deborah had feared, the young man seemed to be after everything she'd pinned her hopes on. He outbid her to the point of lunacy on several things.

She felt her fury rising. It was unfair of someone like him to patronise the local sales. No-one in the district could afford prices like that.

Amanda was probably right. He must be into the American market, and in that case should be in the city where he belonged.

WHEN the sale was halfway through and she had only been able to buy the minimum of the items she'd wanted, at a maximum price, a worm of an idea entered her head.

She waited until the auctioneer held up an album of old photographs that she knew were of little value.

"Shall we start the bidding at a pound?" he asked breezily. A ripple of laughter floated round the room.

Deborah made her bid more than usually clear. She raised her hand instead of giving her usual nod.

The auctioneer gave a smile in her direction. He was about to bring his hammer down.

What happened in the next instant was what Deborah had hoped.

"Two pounds!" The young man at the back of the hall spoke up loudly.

Deborah raised her hand again.

"Three pounds! Thank you, madam. The bidding's with you again, sir!"

Deborah gave a small smile of satisfaction. Her scheme was working nicely.

Against the young man's bidding she brought the price up to £10 before she slowly shook her head and allowed the hammer to fall in the young man's direction.

She immediately felt Amanda's eyes on her.

"You crafty old thing," the older woman whispered. "I believe you meant him to have it all the time. I must say I admire your nerve. I'd have been too afraid to try a trick like that in case I got landed instead."

Deborah gave a deprecating shrug. She was very pleased with herself but she wasn't going to show it.

"It was quite a pretty album. I do hope he appreciates my generosity in letting him have it."

Amanda disguised a smile.

"Oh, I'm sure he will!"

But towards the end of the sale Debbie's self-satisfaction had disappeared. She had lost the pedestal table she had set her heart on to the young man. And she was absolutely furious.

Well, now she would teach him a lesson he wouldn't forget.

The hideous picture that the auctioneer held up gave her a golden opportunity.

Partway through the bidding the rest of the dealers lost interest. The picture was going to fall to the young man for a price of £10. Raising her hand, she brought the price up swiftly, to £15. Once again they were locked in battle for possession.

Only Amanda guessed what was in Deborah's mind. The rest of the dealers looked askance as the bidding rose to £35.

THE BEST OF THE BARGAINS

Deborah kept her head clear. She was taking a gamble. If it paid off, her feeling of satisfaction would be worth it.

She even began to feel a giddy sense of power when she brought the price up to her final breath-taking bid.

"Forty-five pounds, madam. The bidding's with you, sir?"

Deborah waited expectantly for the young man to raise the price to £50.

When nothing happened she felt a sharp moment of panic.

She turned quickly to see his attention captured by something that was happening outside the window.

Hurry — oh — hurry! she told him by mental telepathy.

"The bidding's with you again, sir?" the auctioneer repeated.

Deborah waited, her heart in her mouth.

When the young man spoke it was certainly not what she expected him to say.

"Oh, look — I'm sorry. I've left my car on a double yellow line. There's a warden eyeing it. I shall have to go!"

She could hardly believe her ears. Grimly she closed her eyes as the hammer fell.

The auctioneer spoke again.

"It's yours, madam, for forty-five pounds. I believe the name's Houghton, isn't it?"

She nodded in bleak dejection. Amanda squeezed her shoulder with compassion.

"Hard lines, dear! It would have struck a nice blow for all of us if only it had come off!"

Deborah ignored her pity.

At the close of sale when she stowed the few things she had bought into her estate car — along with the grotesque picture she had never really wanted — she drove off into the country.

She felt sick every time she thought of the ridiculous amount of money she had wasted.

It had been a ludicrous trick. She had intended to teach the young man a lesson, but instead it had rebounded on her.

She had seen him again just as she left the hall. He had stopped and started to say a few words to her, but she had swept past without looking or listening to him, carrying the horrible object under her arm.

She had driven off straightaway, not even bothering to speak to any of the other dealers.

Now she sat motionless in her car, looking out of the window forlornly at some cows grazing in a nearby field.

She heaved a desperate sigh.

It was no use crying over spilt milk. She had brought the whole thing on herself. It had really been a despicable thing she had tried to do.

It was clear that whether the young man was into the American market or not, he was a complete beginner. No-one else would have paid the ridiculous prices he'd paid.

Perhaps, with a bit of luck, he would leave the district soon and things would get back to normal. She would go on buying and selling in the usual way until she was as old as Charlie Allsorts.

That thought didn't please her at all.

She glanced in the driving mirror. Clear brown eyes looked back. They were set in a small, heart-shaped face. Suddenly she saw the rich colour of her hair change to grey like Amanda Heering's. A few wrinkles etched their way across her forehead.

She gave a gasp of horror. The image disappeared.

Pull yourself together, she told herself. Stop feeling so self-pitying. It's time you were home. Bun will be wondering where you are.

THE BEST OF THE BARGAINS

Starting up the car, she realised she had driven in a roundabout route from Penbury. It would mean going through Dabworthy. It would give her a chance to look at Charlie Allsorts' shop.

Maybe, by now, there would be a saleboard outside. That, in itself, was a depressing thought.

THE small village was about the same size as her own. Charlie's black and white timbered property was in a prime position. The name above the fascia board — ALLSORTS — wasn't really his surname. She had never known what it was. Everyone in the trade referred to him as either old Charlie — or Charlie Allsorts. He had seemed to be all alone in the world and it had been a shock to learn he had relatives.

She stopped the car outside, relieved to see no sign of a For Sale notice.

Getting out, she peered curiously through the mullioned windows. The amount of pieces in the showroom surprised her. According to Bunny, it should have been run down. But he had a far better display than her.

She twisted her head to read some of the prices on the articles and gave a whistle of disbelief. Charlie must have been ill. He couldn't possibly expect to get the price he'd named on that tag.

Yet some of the other prices were ridiculously cheap. Maybe she had read them wrongly.

She peered again to make sure. At the same moment she heard the sound of a bell as the shop door opened beside her.

When she looked up she saw the same young man from the saleroom smiling down.

Surprise made her blurt without thinking — "You! What on earth are you doing here?"

The man gave a laugh. "I was thinking the same about you. But I'd like to add — what a delightful surprise!"

She found herself colouring.

"What I meant to say was I thought the shop was closed. I happen to know Charlie's ill. I sent him a get well card a few days ago to Shropshire."

"My home county." The young man's eyes twinkled. "That was very kind of you. I hope he appreciates it."

Deborah frowned. "Just who are you?"

The man put out his hand.

"I'm David Faulds. Charlie Faulds in my great-uncle. I'm trying to keep the place going while he's staying with my parents."

Deborah felt her hand clutched in his.

"And you're Deborah Houghton. My uncle's mentioned you."

He examined her face for a full few seconds, still holding her hand. With embarrassment she pulled it away.

"I feel I owe you an apology," the young man went on. "I imagine you must think I've been making a bit of a nuisance of myself."

He gave her another disarming smile. "I can explain — if only you'll let me."

"I really haven't the time," she said distantly.

"Oh — that's a pity." He sounded disappointed. "My uncle thought highly of you. He told me you were different from the other dealers. He even said you might help me."

She regarded him questioningly, and the young man went on awkwardly.

"You see — when I offered to look after his business he told me to look out for you. Actually, he mentioned an extremely attractive girl with deep brown eyes. He said I couldn't go wrong if I followed your lead at the auctions and bid for the same items as you . . ."

Deborah opened her mouth with astonishment.

". . . I know nothing about antiques, you see," David continued. "I'm an art

145

THE BEST OF THE BARGAINS

teacher, as a matter of fact. This happens to coincide with my long overdue holiday."

His expression took on a wistful look.

"I really thought you wouldn't mind too much if I used your superior knowledge and stocked up . Uncle Charlie's shop with a few things to keep him in business until he came back.

"But — if I've been too greedy and stolen too many things you wanted — I'm extremely sorry," he added quickly.

She was lost for words. The man's honesty was off-putting. It made her flush with shame when she remembered the incident of the album and the ridiculous picture.

She turned her attention to the window to hide her expression.

"Don't you know anything about antiques at all?"

He laughed. "Not a thing. But I'm working at it — reading various books and things. I'm hoping to keep the fort going until he returns."

She gave a small smile.

"Well, you won't be too successful if you let some of the pieces go at these prices." There was a teasing note in her voice, but the young man knew she was serious.

"Then I wonder if you could possibly help me to re-price things?"

She stared at him. To her surprise she found herself agreeing and David's pleasure at this was obvious. In the shop, surrounded by the kind of items she usually stocked, it was a simple job, with her professional knowledge, to re-price the items more realistically.

Displaying his gratitude, he took her arm, and said, "Come on — I'll treat you to lunch in the pub across the road."

She freed herself gently. "I really must be getting back. My sister will be worried. She's only seventeen. I don't like leaving her in charge for too long."

"Then what about coming out to dinner with me this evening?" he asked quickly.

She caught his earnest insistence, and a traitorous voice in her head told her what nice, warm, blue eyes he had.

"Thank you. That would be nice," she said softly.

"I'll bring along a book that might interest you," he said, trying unsuccessfully to hide his excitement. "It's one on paintings. I suppose you already know that the picture I let you have is worth about three times the amount you paid for it. I do happen to know a little about art. As I said, it's my subject."

She gave a gasp. She had already forgotten about the picture. Caught up in the

THE BEST OF THE BARGAINS

looks he was giving her, antiques were beginning to take a back seat in her mind.

Vaguely she heard him go on.

"In fact, I can introduce you to a friend of mine who'll probably buy it. Perhaps you'd let me drive you to London on Sunday. We could mix business with pleasure."

Deborah dropped her eyes, her heart racing. This was all happening too fast for her to comprehend. She was unsure exactly what was happening, only that she was experiencing something new and rather wonderful.

"We'll discuss it this evening," she said briefly.

His ecstatic smile told her they'd probably be discussing much more pleasant topics, too.

As she waved to him and drove off, she tried to analyse the novel and totally intoxicating sensation.

David, watching her until she disappeared into the distance, had already analysed the feeling. He'd been in love with her since the first moment he'd set eyes on her.

Only one cloud marred his horizon. He was generally truthful, and he had told her a white lie when he had said his uncle had asked him to look out for her. Following her lead in the saleroom had been the best way he could think of for capturing her attention.

But his singing heart rapidly drove the small grey cloud over the edge of the skyline.

From what he had gathered over the past week, everything was fair in love and auction sales. □

A TOUCH OF SCOTLAND

A crofter's cottage low in the
hills, amidst a sea of heather,
Sweet smelling mist, rolling over
both, that warns of autumn
weather;
The snug tight thatch rests, moss
endowed, upon the cottage
white,
Its latticed windows and worn
oak door hold warm, a soft
firelight;
A startled cry rings out to warn,
within the glens of dew,
A grouse sinks low in misty
grass, to see the danger through;
A peacefulness descends the
hills, the only gentle sound,
A waterfall, that splashes soft, to
granite lichen, ground.

Mrs J. Byrne, Ipswich.

AUTUMN LEAVES

The whispers of the peaceable breeze
quivering the vermilion leaves,
Each one trembling to cleave to the
bough,
Before spiralling on their meandrous
expedition,
To enshroud the grass in a blanket of
rich, blazing colour.
Silently lying dormant, biding time until
the erratic, crisp squalls
Come to rush them upwards in the
whirlpool and tang of smoky air,
Escaping the fervent flame of the
gardener's inferno,
Eluding for a short while to soar tall in
the autumnal blustering,
Finally succumbing to alight in
secluded and shadowy corners,
Lonesome leafage lingering . . . for just
a moment more.

Mrs E. Stevenson, Inverness

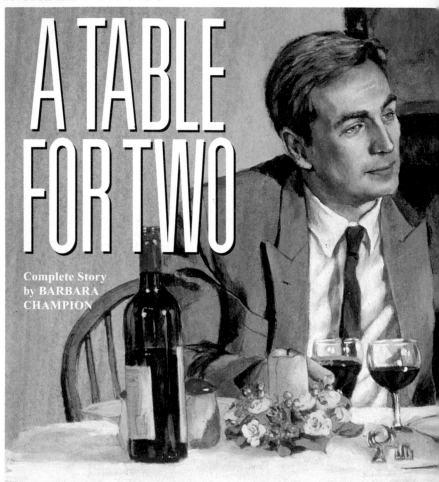

A TABLE FOR TWO

Complete Story
by BARBARA
CHAMPION

It wasn't so much a lunch date as a council of war — and neither of them had come prepared for a truce!

GERARD DIXON was one of those reliable young men who always had to be in command — of himself in every situation. Essentially self-reliant, clearly in full control of his own destiny, he was well dressed, well mannered and seriously handsome.

Gerard did not conform. Nobody could say with any certainty where he would be or what he would be doing at any particular time of day. He was a loner.

148

A TABLE FOR TWO

He had been with the firm three months and he was known in the canteen as "The Incredible Ideas Man" by all those who talked behind his back . . . and that was unavoidable because he'd never been in the canteen.

That's not entirely true, because he made a quick tour of the tables Friday lunch-time while looking for Miss Isherwood, but had made a rapid exit when it became clear she wasn't there.

Nobody knew exactly what he did but his name was on a door on the

149

A TABLE FOR TWO

sixth floor. Rumour had it that he did all the foreign wheeling and dealing and had three packed flight bags; one in his flat, one in his office and one in his car, a rather fancy Italian job.

Which brings us to the matter of the car.

He would have liked to be able to park his car nearer to the firm's offices than a mile away, or preferably within the firm's inadequate car park, or better still — in Miss Laurel Isherwood's reserved parking space.

Laurel Isherwood did not know this, but then she didn't know Mr Dixon either.

She'd seen him a few times in the corridors, of course, but as his appointment with the firm had been conducted at top level, she'd never met him. After all, his office was on the sixth floor, while hers was only the third.

As Personnel Officer, she did assist with selecting suitable applicants for routine vacancies but in the main she handled their working problems and quite frequently, their domestic dramas as well.

For someone as young as she (after all, she was only in her mid-twenties), she seemed to be able to understand and solve other people's problems surprisingly well.

But outside office hours she rarely mixed with the rest of the staff; and indeed, to everyone at Wender & Wender Imports Ltd., she was rather an unknown quantity.

Sometimes one of the young directors — Dougie Baker — slid into the opposite seat and unloaded the traumas of his long-running romance with an air-hostess called Rosie. But Laurel seldom made much comment.

Laurel was not a great talker but she was a good listener and men seemed to like that. She was also bright, efficient and coolly attractive.

It was Dougie who told Gerard where Laurel Isherwood spent her lunch hours.

"She's a bit dry though," he said, "never talks much . . . a bit prim — not your type at all . . ."

"Thanks!" Gerard said as he walked away.

Gerard Dixon liked to get his facts right and intended to check on the parking situation at that very moment.

Yes, there it was!

Laurel Isherwood had left her blue bicycle, complete with saddle-bag and shopping basket, right smack in the middle of her parking spot.

She had acquired an oblong concrete slab which was equipped with a steel eye and a long groove, thus allowing her to place the front wheel of her bike in the groove and to chain the frame to the steel eye.

"All very clever, very functional and completely selfish!" mused Gerard.

During his comings and goings he'd often seen Miss Isherwood in the company of her bicycle.

When she was on it she wore a navy-blue trouser outfit and reminded him of a Tour de France loser; when she was off it she wore black-tailored suits and frilly blouses and reminded him of a traffic warden with lace.

A TABLE FOR TWO

T Au Roi Neptune he spotted her at once, lunching alone. Fearlessly, sensing no apprehension, Gerard approached Laurel Isherwood and addressed the lady in question.

"May I join you?"

She didn't answer so he sat down.

"I'm Gerard Dixon . . . sixth floor," he said, "we've never been introduced." He smiled.

Miss Isherwood appraised him from over the top of her wine glass.

"I've seen you around," she said.

Although not immune to the chill in the air, Gerard consulted the menu.

"Is the chicken any good?" His voice was steady and, he hoped, friendly.

"I've no idea, this is a speciality fish restaurant."

"Ahhh! Then I'll have lamb chops," Gerard stubbornly replied, unwilling even to acknowledge his mistake.

The waiter arrived and he ordered.

Laurel Isherwood silently inspected the man. She thought he looked strong, efficient and arrogant.

"Forgive me for interrupting your lunch, Miss Isherwood," he began, "but I wanted to talk to you in an informal atmosphere." He paused when she didn't look up. "And I need your help."

"Oh, yes?" she said, still not looking up.

"It's your bike," Gerard continued, despite her disinterest. "It takes up a lot of room."

"I sold my car," Miss Isherwood stated bluntly.

"So I gathered." He was beginning to be a little irritated by her manner.

"They pollute," she continued.

"That's true," Gerard agreed, patiently. "And you're happy now with your bicycle?" Humouring her seemed to be the best policy.

"Yes," she said, still in her very matter-of-fact manner. "But it's still only an experiment, I haven't faced a winter on two wheels yet."

"So you might buy another car?"

"I might."

"And is that why you have your concrete stand placed centrally in your parking space?"

"That's right," Laurel dabbed at the corners of her mouth with her napkin and Gerard couldn't help noticing her beautifully manicured hands.

Also, her thick, glossy hair, although long, was beautifully neat and tidy.

"And I don't want anybody trying to push me out," she said, looking him straight in the eye.

"Aahhh! Well now, that's what I wanted to talk to you about," Gerard said. "If you were to park your bicycle sideways, flat against the wall . . . I could park behind you."

"The new Executive Car Park will be completed in six months' time." There was no ignoring her dismissive tone.

"Right," Gerard, determined not to give up, "but meantime I have to park anything up to a mile away and as I'm not at the office every day there is no specific place for me . . . yet."

Suddenly she pushed her chair gently away from the table and instead of rising, looked him straight in the eye.

"Are you as healthy and athletic as you look. Mr . . . er . . . Dixon?" she enquired, in a musing tone.

"I'm pretty fit. I work-out a lot and play squash." He grinned, thinking he could see the way her mind was working. "But if you're going to suggest that I should walk to and from work for the sake of my health I'm afraid there just isn't time."

"No." Laurel Isherwood flashed him a stunningly uncharacteristic smile. "I was going to suggest that you painted my ceiling."

The unflappable, unshakeable Gerard Dixon — who thought he'd heard it all — almost choked on a piece of lamp chop in his surprise.

"I've emulsioned all the walls in my flat," she explained, "but I couldn't manage the ceilings."

Gerard still couldn't manage to speak.

"I suffer from vertigo," she confessed.

Gerard coughed and pushed his plate away from him.

"Ceilings?" he queried.

"Yes, four . . . didn't I say four?" The air of innocence she'd adopted was quite transparent.

"Couldn't one of your friends give you a hand?" he asked, ungallantly.

"I think not," Miss Isherwood said. "Tom Arnett once aspired to help me erect some shelves and knocked half the plaster off the wall in the process. No, no." She smiled. "I need somebody strong and reliable — somebody who knows what he's doing."

It was very obvious flattery and yet Gerard couldn't help feeling pleased by her words.

"But you're evidently too busy." She stood up. "Pity . . . still, it was just a thought." She smiled and leaving a whiff of delicious perfume behind, she departed.

GERARD ordered banana fritters and congratulated himself on disposing of Miss Laurel Isherwood. She was pulling my strings and it didn't work, he told himself.

Mind you, she had very beautiful eyes and very delicate hands.

Later that afternoon he telephoned Laurel Isherwood.

"Have you all the necessary paints to hand?" he asked.

"Of course, Mr Dixon," she replied cheerfully, "and brushes and steps."

"Then perhaps I'd better come by and check on what you've been up to. Would this evening be convenient?" he queried.

"Fine," she agreed. "About eight o'clock if you like."

"That sounds all right."

"Good, I'll expect you," she said. "Flat three, twelve Laburnum Close."

Gerard didn't bother to tell her that he'd already checked up on where she lived. And he wasn't giving into her manipulation. He was merely using it to his own good — the means to an end!

But, when the time came, Gerard had not been expecting to be greeted by a young woman in tight red jeans and a long sweater with shiny brown hair streaming down her back. She glowed and he could tell she'd just stepped out of the shower. Desperately trying not to appear completely thrown, Gerard inspected her interior decorations with a serious, businesslike expression.

They were good, very good. But, of course, he couldn't tell her that.

"You should have done the ceilings first," he challenged.

"I know that now," she answered, not in the least put out.

Trying not to look at her too much, he became aware of a delicious aroma, obviously emanating from what he guessed must be the kitchen.

Laurel Isherwood, as alert as ever, noticed his preoccupation. "Would you like some?" she asked.

"What is it?" His enquiry was casual, but his hunger wasn't.

"Oh, just a bean curry I threw together," she said.

In her cosy kitchen alcove, on high stools at a breakfast bar, with Laurel's black kitten continually climbing up his trouser leg, they demolished the curry and Gerard had to admit it was excellent.

Indeed, he became so relaxed and comfortable that he agreed to paint all her ceilings for her on Saturday afternoon, providing she parked her bicycle sideways, as from the following Monday.

O N the Saturday, when he called at the flat, dressed in overalls, a neighbour was waiting to let him in. "Laurel has had to visit a friend," he was told. "She'll be back fairly soon. She did say that could you please mind the carpets with drips?"

Despite the fact that he was treated like an odd-job man, Gerard reflected that perhaps it was best to remain formal.

In silence, completely unaided and strangely lonely, he painted the ceilings, touched up the walls here and there and finally, rinsed the brushes under the cold tap.

At exactly the same time Laurel entered complete with kitten in a basket and accompanied by the stirring aroma of fish and chips.

"I went mad and bought us fish and chips," she told him gaily. It was strange — the more he saw of Laurel, the more attractive she became to him.

Leaving him to split the paper package onto two dinner plates, she then wandered through the flat and loudly admired his work.

"Why, it's wonderful, Gerard," she called. "It's marvellous, really very well done."

She was wearing jeans again and a T-shirt, with her hair tied up in a long pony-tail.

He was growing accustomed to seeing her like this, and decided he rather liked it.

Not having tasted fish and chips for years, Gerard was astonished to find it so delicious.

As she plopped the plates in a bowl of hot suds Laurel said, "I'll do the washing-up later . . . I must rush and get changed, I've got an appointment."

A TABLE FOR TWO

They shook hands across the threshold of her front door and too breezily Gerard Dixon said:

"I'll see you around . . . er . . . Laurel."

"Most probably, Gerard," she agreed, with a bright smile.

ON Monday morning Gerard arrived in the office car park in time to see the caretaker dragging Laurel Isherwood's bicycle-stand complete with bike into a sideways situation against the wall. He waved to Gerard and called him forward.

"There you are, Mr Dixon," he said, "all arranged now."

That afternoon Gerard had a conference with his boss, and discovered he would have to go to Portsmouth for a week on business. There was the chance of obtaining two substantial contracts with important clients in that area.

Just seven days later he was travelling home again with the contracts safely tucked away in his executive briefcase.

Glancing at the leather case on the passenger seat beside him, he felt quite pleased with himself. But — only quite.

He was still puzzling over this lack of self-satisfaction when he drew into the office car park.

Suddenly, all thoughts left his mind, to be replaced by furious all-consuming anger.

"I don't believe it! I just don't believe it!" he shouted out loud.

Fuming, he swung himself out of the car and walked over to the parking space that should have been his.

There, resting, rather arrogantly, he thought, in its stand, was Miss Laurel Isherwood's gleaming cycle.

How could she, he thought. After all he'd done for the smug little madam! Well, she certainly wouldn't be smug by the time he was finished with her!

In the corridor of Wender & Wender Imports Ltd., heads turned in amazement as Gerard Dixon, "The Incredible Ideas Man", strode through the reception area and summoned the lift with a violent stab of his fist. His fury was indeed a sight to behold!

And none were more unashamedly curious than Tom Arnett and Miss Peters. Open-mouthed, they watched the lift travel to the third floor, then

stop. Turning to look at each other, neither spoke, but both headed for the stairs to discover more.

On the third floor Gerard hastily discovered the right door and without knocking threw it open so hard it bounced back again after he'd stepped into the room.

Miss Laurel Isherwood was not a lady easily perturbed, but in that second her reaction could only be described as rather shocked.

She'd been seated at her desk when the door flew open so forcibly, but now she was on her feet, papers on the floor, where she'd knocked them from her desk at his unexpected entrance.

However, in a second she was her usual unruffled self and if Gerard noticed any apprehension in her eyes he chose to ignore it.

"Miss Isherwood!" he stormed. "What exactly is your bicycle doing in my parking space?"

"You'll remember we had an agreement, Mr Dixon." Her voice was almost, but not quite, level. "I would let you use my space — temporarily, if you would paint my ceilings . . ."

"Yes." He had intended the word to be sharp, but somehow it didn't come out that way.

"Well . . ." She hesitated, and taking a few steps round her desk, stood firmly in front of him.

Her eyes really were the softest shade of grey, he thought irrationally.

"Well . . .?" he enquired, folding his arms in what he hoped was a formidable way.

"Well," she repeated, raising her shapely head in a dignified manner. "The ceilings you painted are streaky!"

For a moment there was silence. Gerard was astounded. It was absolutely absurd.

Then, unable to resist it, he began to laugh. He laughed and laughed so hard his sides began to ache and tears came to his eyes.

Finally he composed himself sufficiently to say, "Well, there's only one thing for it — I'll just have to do them again."

"Yes," she agreed. "I'm afraid you must."

Together they laughed heartily and Gerard realised he'd missed her. That was why his success had seemed so hollow.

Outside the door, two people listened to the sound of merriment, just as baffled by the hilarity as they'd been by the shouting they'd heard when they'd arrived on the third floor.

When at last the laughter stopped and all was quiet their curiosity overcame them and peeping round the half-open door, the most amazing sight met their eyes.

Mr Dixon was kissing Miss Isherwood — and very passionately too! Tom Arnett chuckled. Sly old Dixon!

Miss Peters' mouth and eyes were like three large Os. Wasn't Miss Isherwood lucky?

And when the two eavesdroppers turned to speak to each other the same words escaped their lips.

"No-one will ever believe us!" they chorused and carefully closing the door, they left the young couple alone. □

A Lesson For Albert

Complete Story By
CAROL MARSH

Yes, even at his age he had a lot to learn — like what being a grandfather really means . . .

ALBERT found the pink rabbit when he was cleaning his flat on Monday morning. A small, fluffy baby toy his son and daughter-in-law had obviously left behind when they brought little Victoria Alice to see him the night before.

His face creasing into lines of thought, Albert held the rabbit on one broad, calloused palm.

He wondered whether it had been missed — if perhaps Victoria Alice (the name still seemed an unnecessary mouthful) had refused to settle in her cot for the night without it.

Even at four months old, he seemed to remember, babies could be remarkably set in their ways. Hadn't there been something about Simon and a green elephant?

He sighed, shaking his head, and his blue eyes went wistfully, automatically, across the small living-room to the framed photograph of his wife, Belle.

Belle would have known immediately what to do about the pink rabbit — just as she would have known instinctively everything else about Victoria Alice, he realised.

And the loss and loneliness that had seeped into every corner of his world since she died, three years ago, made him catch his breath anew.

Placing the toy on the sideboard, he went through to the bedroom to prepare for his usual outing.

On Mondays, now he was retired, he usually put on his corduroys and walked down to his allotment before stopping in at the Crown and Anchor for a lunch-time pie and a pint.

Or, if it was raining, he wore his second-best suit and went to the library and the brightly-lit shopping precinct.

It wasn't raining today, yet for some reason Albert still put on his second-best suit. As he walked back into the silence of the living-room, the pink rabbit on the sideboard seemed almost to leap out at him, soft and new, and totally out of place.

As he picked it up again, Albert realised, in spite of himself, that those words *out of place* described exactly how he himself had felt for the past four months.

Becoming a grandparent had turned out so disappointingly different to what Belle had always said it would be.

Though Simon and Melanie brought Victoria Alice to see him every Sunday evening, and had invited him over to their smart, detached house several times since the elaborate christening party, Albert had always felt aware of a gap between them.

As if, pleasant though the atmosphere always was, the visits to the flat and the carefully-spaced invitations were more a matter of polite duty than anything else.

And as for Victoria Alice, in whose honour it was all supposed to be — each time he had seen her so far, she had been fast asleep, her small, pale face and curling fists reminding him of a tiny, unopened flower.

She was infinitely too delicate, especially in all her lace finery, for a big, clumsy man like him to touch without supervision . . .

SUDDENLY reaching a decision, Albert went into the hall and put on his overcoat. He would go to the telephone box at the end of the street and ring his son's house.

A LESSON FOR ALBERT

Then, he'd know for certain whether the rabbit could be safely left with him until next Sunday's visit.

As an afterthought, he pushed the toy into his pocket. And later, standing in the phone box listening to the "number unobtainable" tone, he realised there was only one thing he could do now.

He had never thought of going round to Simon's uninvited before, especially on a Monday morning when he would definitely not be expected. Not at all.

But now, the weight of the pink rabbit in his pocket, together with the frustrating, jarring note of the telephone, seemed to spur him on to the house.

As he walked, he felt himself growing strangely nervous, realising that with Simon out at work, Melanie would be at home on her own.

Straightening his back, Albert attempted a carefree whistle, reminding

himself that for all her college education and clever way of speaking, his daughter-in-law was a sweet girl — kind, caring and sensible.

He recalled, with another stab of pain, how happy Belle had been when they married.

"I couldn't have chosen anyone better for Simon myself!" she'd said, beaming, as she hugged Melanie, who looked like a dainty little sprite in her white wedding dress. "You're just the girl I would have chosen to be the mother of my grandchildren . . . !"

Poor Belle! In that tender, teasing moment, when Melanie blushed, and Simon declared, "Give us time, Mum!" none of them had known she wouldn't live to see the birth of the miracle she had so looked forward to.

His thoughts returned to Victoria Alice, and Albert sighed. As he approached the housing estate where Simon and Melanie lived, his fingers curled around the rabbit in his pocket.

Were all small babies so perfect and untouchable, he wondered. Had it been like that with Simon, when Belle, at her most committed and energetic, had been in charge?

He shook his head with the effort of trying to remember so far back, and the only memory that came was a recent one. Of Melanie, her smooth and lovely face annoyed, taking Simon to task at the flat last Sunday.

"Oh, for goodness' sake, Simon, don't say you forgot to put the bibs in

158

the bag after all! I asked you specially . . . Now, I'll have to tuck tissues round her neck while I feed her!"

"Tissues? Er — will paper hankies do . . . ?" Albert had said.

As Melanie nodded and smiled her thanks, he'd watched her handling baby and bottle, the slight flush still on her face, and again he'd felt that sense of awe and wonder.

As if, as an outsider, he were watching a ritual he might possibly witness, but never once participate in.

Now he slowly approached the smart street. Curtains were drawn across gleaming picture windows, and the only people in sight were young, smartly-dressed women, weeding their gardens or walking, children in tow, to the shops.

Not for the first time since he retired, Albert felt alone in a land where he had no place.

He swallowed, wondering why on earth he had come.

He would ring the bell, hand the toy to Melanie and then leave, saying he had to go to his allotment.

Melanie would obviously be too busy with coffee mornings or amateur-dramatics friends to want to bother with him.

Feeling stupidly like a school-boy on an errand, he rang the bell and waited. And waited . . .

FINALLY, after a few moments, the door opened a crack, and Melanie peered out. But this was a Melanie he had never seen before; still in her dressing-gown, her neat fair hair all dishevelled — and the marks of recent tears on her face.

From inside the house, Albert could hear the sound of high-pitched, persistent, ear-splitting wailing.

"D-Dad!" Melanie exclaimed, as Albert, forgetting his bashfulness, stepped into the hall. She pulled the untidy dressing-gown around her, and pushed ineffectually at her hair. "I — I wasn't expecting . . . Oh, that noise! Come in, please."

Albert followed her, pulling the rabbit out of his pocket as explanation. When he got into the living-room, Melanie was sitting on the sofa with her head in her hands, and Victoria Alice was still screaming her head off in her cot in the corner.

"I . . . I can't seem to stop her," the young woman said, her voice shaking on the edge of tears again, as she rose and picked the yelling, kicking bundle up.

"She's not wet or hungry, but she just won't stop when she cries like this! And just look at the place! I haven't even cleared her bath away yet, and there's the shopping — and the phone's out of order, and Simon asked me to report it. And — oh, no — the milkman's at the door now — and —"

Breaking off mid-sentence, she looked around distractedly just as Albert, not knowing what else to do, put the pink rabbit on top of a pile of

A LESSON FOR ALBERT

other soft toys on the armchair.

Next moment, to his amazement, he found himself being unceremoniously handed the baby, screams and all.

"Here — hang on . . ." he began, panic rising in him. As Melanie rushed past him, he looked fearfully down at the crying bundle in his arms. And immediately, miraculously, Victoria Alice stopped crying.

Awe-stricken, Albert moved slowly backwards through the chaos he never thought he'd see in Simon and Melanie's home, and lowered himself gingerly on to the sofa.

Almost afraid to breathe, he tickled the baby's tummy with his forefinger. She immediately found it and curled her tiny fist around the finger in a surprisingly firm grip. Hiccuping, she blinked up at him, and his heart turned right over.

"Her grandmother's eyes," he was saying wonderingly, unsteadily, as Melanie came back into the room a moment later. "She — she's got Belle's blue eyes. I never knew!"

Melanie nodded, as she quickly removed the baby bath. "I know," she said. She seemed much more in control now the crying had stopped, and through the dawning wonder and excitement inside him, Albert remembered what Belle used to say, about women often being weepy after babies were born. About the responsibility and hard work of it all.

"I often remember what — what Mum always said — about me being the perfect mother," Melanie said now, hesitantly, a flush mounting her cheeks. "But I'm not — I — I'm hopeless, most of the time."

In a flash of understanding, Albert realised what the carefully-arranged visits, the immaculate clothes, the always angelic, spotless baby meant.

Melanie had been as nervous of him, in her own way, as he had been of her and the baby.

"Maybe you've just been trying too hard, love," he said. "Nobody and nothing's perfect, you know — and a bloomin' good job, too, I reckon!"

As Victoria Alice blasted him again with those devastating blue eyes, his heart swelled with wonder and pride — and fresh hope for the future.

"If you'd like a break, on a regular basis, I mean," he said awkwardly as Melanie's face lit up with surprise and pleasure, "I could wheel her down to my allotment and back . . . ?"

Later, carefully, and somehow expertly, pushing the gleaming new pram, he felt 10 feet tall.

All the joy that Belle had promised in her love and wisdom, was reaching him at last. □

TOPSY TURVY

The little girl in your life will have double the fun playing with this upside-down doll

Materials Required – Of **Sirdar Country Style Double Knit**

2 x 50 gram balls main for pink doll (we chose parasol pink) and 2 x 50 gram balls main for blue doll (saxe), 1 x 50 gram ball of each of the following 4 colours: naturelle, banana, majestic mink and white; one pair of 4 mm (No. 8) knitting needles; 76 cm, *30 inches,* of 2 cm, *⁴⁄₄-inch*, wide white broderie anglaise; 1.75 metres, *2 yards,* of 5 cm, *2-inch*, wide gathered broderie anglaise; 1.70 metres, *1⅞ yards*, of 1.5 cm, *⅝-inch*, wide white ribbon; washable toy stuffing; blue, white and black embroidery threads. *For best results it is essential to use the recommended yarn. If you have difficulty in obtaining the yarn, write direct, enclosing a stamped, addressed envelope to the following address for stockists: Sirdar PLC, Flanshaw Lane, Alverthorpe, Wakefield, Yorkshire WF2 9ND.*

Measurement – Top of head to bottom of dress 51 cm, *20 inches.*

Abbreviations – **K** – knit; **st.(s)** – stitch(es); **st.-st.** – stocking-stitch; **tog.** – together; **g.-st.** – garter stitch; **cm** – centimetres; **P** – parasol pink; **N** – naturelle; **W** – white; **B** – saxe blue; **Y** – banana.

PINK DOLL

Body

With P cast on 60 sts. and work 25 rows st.-st. Change to N and work 29 rows.

Next row — K2 tog. to end. Break off yarn, leaving a long end, thread

162

end through remaining sts. and leave.

Arms (Two)

With P cast on 3 sts. and work in st.-st. Increase 1 st. at each end of 2nd and following 4 alternate rows. Work 5 rows.

Change to N and work a further 23 rows. Finish as for body.

Skirt (Two Pieces The Same)

With P cast on 75 sts. and knit 6 rows. Continue in P and beginning with a knit row work 85 rows st.-st. Break off yarn, thread end through sts. and leave.

Neck Frill

With W cast on 80 sts. knit 2 rows.

Next row — K2 tog. to end of row. Beginning with a purl row, work 3 rows st.-st. Cast off.

Waist Frill

With W cast on 110 sts. and knit 2 rows.

Next row — K2 tog. to end. Beginning with a purl row work 5 rows st.-st. Cast off.

Sleeve Frill (Two)

With W cast on 30 sts. and knit 2 rows.

Next row — K2 tog. to end. Cast off.

BLUE DOLL

Body

Work as for pink doll but use B and N.

Arms (Two)

With B cast on 3 sts. and work in st.-st. Increase 1 st. at each end of 2nd and following 4 alternate rows. Still with B work a further 21 rows. Change to N and work 7 rows. Finish as for body.

Skirt

Work the same as for pink doll's skirt but use B.

Collar

With Y cast on 52 sts. and work in g.-st. Decrease 1 st. at each end of the 2nd and following 3 alternate rows.

Cast off.

Cuffs (Two)

With Y cast on 10 sts. and work 26 rows st.-st. Cast off.

Apron

With W cast on 50 sts. and work 54 rows st.-st. Cast off 15 sts. at beginning of next 2 rows. Continue on remaining 20 sts. for bib, work 16 rows. Cast off.

Pockets (Two)

With W cast on 10 sts. and work 10 rows st.-st. Cast off.

Shoes (For Both Dolls)

Work two pieces in P and two pieces in B. Cast on 12 sts. and work 8 rows st.-st. Decrease 1 st. at each end of next 4 rows.

Cast off remaining 4 sts.

To Make Up

Join seam of body of pink doll. Stuff. Pull up yarn at top of head and fasten off securely. Take a matching length of yarn and tie tightly round neck to form head. Repeat with body of blue doll. Join base of bodies together. Join seams of pink skirt. Put on doll. Pull up yarn at top edge of skirt round waist and secure. Repeat with blue skirt. Pull up yarn at bottom of arms, join seams and stuff. Sew matching arms to each side of body, 1.2 cm down from neck edge.

To Complete Pink Doll

Put neck frill round neck edge. Join seam and secure. Repeat with waist frill and sleeve frills. On skirt, using banana yarn, embroider crosses to represent small flowers, and at different intervals embroider larger flowers as shown in picture. Using white cotton (this is neater) sew a

a desired shape. Embroider mouth with pink yarn, eyebrows with brown yarn.

For hair make a "curl" by winding brown yarn round 4 fingers 8 times. Make a further 5 curls and attach to forehead position. Cut through curls thus making a fringe. Cut 114 x 81 cm lengths of brown yarn. Take several lengths at a time, start at front of head (covering stitching of curls) and stitch them securely to head. Cover well, to about 3 cm up from neck edge. Take one set of strands and stitch to one side of head near neck. Repeat with other side. Divide strands into 3 and make a plait at each side. Tie matching yarn round ends of plaits. Trim ends. Take a 30 cm length of white ribbon and make a bow. Stitch below neck frill at centre front.

To Complete Blue Doll

Stitch collar round neck. With right sides facing, place cuffs round wrists and stitch. Stitch up seam about 6 mm. Fold back cuff towards arm of doll. Cut a length of ribbon to fit round neck of apron, stitch to bib. Take remaining ribbon and stitch across bottom of bib to tie at back. Using white cotton stitch the 2 cm wide broderie anglaise round edge of apron skirt and to each side of bib.

Make features as for pink doll. (Use banana yarn instead of brown for eyebrows.)

Embroider small circles in banana down front of dress for buttons. Put apron on doll. For hair, wind banana yarn round 3 fingers 5 times to form "curl". Secure to head. Repeat until you have covered the head.

length of 5 cm wide gathered broderie anglaise to skirt approximately 13 cm down from waist. Sew the remaining length of broderie anglaise towards base of skirt approximately 2.5 cm up from hem.

Stitch pink shoes to blue shoes leaving an opening, and stuff slightly. With blue shoes towards you stitch them between hems of both skirts at centre front about 1.2 cm apart. Stitch both skirts together.

Embroider eyes as in picture. Outline the whole eye with black embroidery thread. Make nose by forming over-stitches and building up

WITHOUT YOU

Complete Story by STELLA WHITELAW

Without You

**An only child away from home for the first time —
of course she was lonely. No, not the daughter, the
mother . . .**

THE telephone sits on the hall table gathering dust. Now it will not
ring incessantly during the cheap-call time, nor stay silent during
the showing of the late-night horror film.

It is not cradled by slim arms and long brown hair, the cord trailing into the sitting-room where secrets are exchanged while sitting on the floor in front of the fire, and sudden fits of giggles ring through the house.

Our car will no longer frequent the local discos and late, late parties. No more chocolate wrappers under the seats, cinema tickets and bottles of nail varnish on the dashboard shelf, my borrowed shawl abandoned on the back seat.

The bathroom is empty, hollow and cold; no eddies of steam defying discreet knocks. Scissors, razor, emery boards will stop walking by themselves.

My protein hair shampoo will shrink in its bottle at a normal rate. Coffee mugs stay in the kitchen when once they spread round the house like mushrooms . . .

The telephone, the car and the bathroom are once more mine. But in their place I have lost a daughter.

Nudging 18, hair like silk, cheeks as pink as country apple blossom and with a ready smile as merry as May, Anna has gone to London.

London, where there are muggers and youths who jostle old ladies on the Underground, parties where drugs are pushed, and I have had to let my daughter go.

London, where she may meet a man and fall in love — tall, short, slim, tubby, policeman or plumber, doctor or docker.

This morning I saw Anna off on the train, the right number of A-levels tucked under her leather belt, eager to put her foot on the first rung of the ladder of success.

And I was only one of thousands of mothers launching their offspring out into the world every year.

Where have all the years gone?

It was only a moment ago that she was a small, crumpled scrap of humanity cradled in my arms; a rosy-cheeked toddler rocking her pram wildly in the back garden; a little girl clinging to my hand as I took her to her first morning at primary school . . .

But this grown-up Anna is laughing, hugging her excitement to herself, eager to be away to the big city, to her new job and independence, to adventure and fun.

"You'd better take a taxi to the flat," I said for the third time. "No point in struggling on the Underground with all that luggage.

"You've put far too much in your tote bag. The handle is going to come adrift."

"I will," she agrees, but her brown eyes are saying: stop fussing, Mother.

She looks so ridiculously young; somewhere between 14 and 16. She cannot possibly be old enough to go away.

What did I do with all the years? All the good advice I meant to give her; the special relationship I was going to build up between her and me.

There wasn't all that much time between working and worrying, and being devoured by the demands of family and house.

"Don't worry about me," she adds. Don't worry, she says.

London is going to swallow my child into its busy throbbing life and I am not to worry.

WE timed it well and there was not long to wait at the station. The train pulled out, taking her eager young face, already turned from home and looking into the future.

I went home, like a sleepwalker, climbed the stairs and now I am in her room.

It is strangely tidy . . . usually one needs an ordnance map to even find her bed. Some tights, wrinkled and forlorn, lie on the carpet.

A room without an owner; only the ghost of a little girl in bed with measles; memories of crawling in on my knees in the dark to fill her Christmas stocking; her solitary hours spent studying in the gloom of O-levels and A-level examinations.

"I hope she'll be all right," I say to the cat. She is Anna's cat and already has the look of a refugee. We comfort each other.

I make myself busy with housework, doing the flowers; then I remember we are going out and there is no need to cook supper.

My husband's firm are holding their annual dinner. We have not gone to it for several years; there's always been a good reason.

But now there is nothing to stop us.

I have a leisurely bath and put on a long dress I haven't worn for years. It still fits me.

I style my hair and find the necklace and earrings Philip gave me for one of our wedding anniversaries. I've never even worn them.

Philip is ready long before me. He looks a stranger in a dinner jacket hired for the occasion.

"Philip, I don't really want to go," I say nervously, clenching and unclenching my hands. "I don't feel like meeting people. It's been an awful day, seeing Anna off to London."

Philip's face clouds over. He is smoking, but not smoking; drinking, but not drinking.

"Beth, you know this evening is important to me. It'll look funny if you don't come."

"I'm sorry, but I'm just not in the mood. I can't make the effort. You don't understand how low I feel.

"This morning at the station, it was as if part of my own body was being torn away. I feel as if I have lost Anna for ever."

"She's my daughter, too," Philip says harshly.

I can tell that he's angry, hurt. But what can I do?

Silence hangs in the room, the dark clouds of a row that does not develop; we are not people who fight.

The telephone rings in the hall. I remember the lines I shall have to say a hundred times to her friends . . .

"No, Anna isn't here anymore. She's left home. Would you like her address? Just a moment . . ."

"Hello, Mum? It's me. Anna. Have you forgotten me already?"

"Anna! I was just so surprised! I thought it would be one of your friends. How are you getting on? Did you manage all right with your luggage?" I gabble the questions.

"Oh, yes. The flat's a bit more untidy than that day we looked at it. But my room's just the same. I'm very lucky." Her voice is still eager, breathless.

Continued on page 170   167

Mother Knows Best

Five highborn ducklings with an unusual family tree follow in Mum's footsteps and cause a bit of a stir in the Strath . . .

IT'S always a sign that summer has come to stay when the little black-faced lambs have grown bigger and gained their independence, no longer clinging very closely and fearfully to their mothers' warm woollen skirts for protection.

They set off on exciting expeditions with other lambs of their own age to explore the rest of this vast world, where they have freedom to do exactly as they please, and the height of their ambition is to throw themselves higher in the air than any of the others, just for the sheer joy of being alive.

On a mound in the middle of the field, they play king, or queen, of the castle, each one trying desperately to stay on top until they are

GIDEON'S WAY

More impressions of life from the Highlands of Scotland, by Gideon Scott May, observer of people and nature alike . . .

dethroned by another.

For a change, the little girl lambs start skipping, while the little boys have bouts of playful head-butting.

Finally, the girls get tired of skipping and the boys finish butting in a friendly way before their heads get too sore, then they all race back to their respective mothers who welcome them with a warm drink and the assurance that, whether or not it had won the skipping or head-butting contests, her baby was still the best of the bunch.

THERE'S a deep dark pool in a backwater of the hill burn, where white water-lilies bob about on the surface with their green skirts spread out.

At my approach, a pair of mallard ducks rise together. The drake is a handsome fellow with colourings of iridescent green, turquoise blue and silver grey, with fiery bronze feathers on his breast.

He has little or no voice and his wife does all the talking with loud quacks.

I guess that their nest must be somewhere near, but my little spotted spaniel with the super-sensitive nose finds it first.

I know immediately by the glittering glance from her left eye, the one surrounded by a black patch, that something is wrong, and as I approach I can see that the nest holds only some sea-green eggshells encircled by a bunch of feathers.

Some passing fox must have pounced on the duck who had just escaped his snapping jaws, so the hungry fox, determined not to leave without a meal,

with golden yellow "sunspots."

But while Mother swam around and around the lily pond, the tiny ducklings looked down and wondered what to do next.

THE baby **d u c k s stayed up in that tree for two more days. They were given frequent "warm-ups" by their mother at night a n d d a i l y demonstrations of how to fly down from the tree.**

All this was to no avail, until the tiny ducklings tired of their confinement, grew restless and jostled each other until one teetered on the edge of the next and tumbled down, frantically fanning the air with its stubby little wings, landing at last with a thump on the soft, springy turf of the burn bank.

Like little paratroopers, the others followed their leader, one by one, until the mother duck and her family were reunited and paddling happily together in the lily pond. □

crunched the eggs and devoured the contents.

I thought the wild duck was sure to go elsewhere after this incident, but I saw her a week later swimming in the lily pool, so I hunted everywhere for her new nest so I could help her conceal it if it was too exposed.

I couldn't find any nest, until I saw Ceilidh sitting underneath the big oak tree by the burn, with her velvety muzzle pointing upwards and a look which plainly said, "And just why didn't you ask *me*?"

I looked up, too, and there was the duck looking down at me from a cleft in the tree almost 12 feet from the ground!

How clever she was, I thought, to sit up there, safe from passing predators. But how, I wondered, was she going to get her babies down from that height?

Ducks' eggs take about a week longer than hens' eggs to hatch, so I knew almost to the day when the "tree babies" would be born and, leaning against the old oak, I looked up expectantly.

The ducklings were there all right, dressed up in dark blue down dappled

"Have you eaten? What did you have for supper?" What a stupid, mothering, smothering question to ask, but it's too late to stop the words.

"Oh, ham salad, but not quite like I'm used to." She sounds slightly less enthusiastic. "And some sort of tart, but it wasn't very filling."

"I suppose everyone watches their figures down there," I say idiotically, wanting to keep her talking.

"Can you bring up my cloak?" she asks, getting to the point of the phone call. "And a spider plant. And some hangers. And would you feel like donating some tea or coffee?"

"Don't they have any shops in London?"

The shot gets home and she laughs. "I haven't had time to go shopping yet. The girls lent me some of theirs, but they say it's best to have your own.

"Just coffee will do," she adds, knowing full well that I will bring both. The list continues, and we arrange a day and time to meet.

"I've got to go now, Mum," she says hurriedly. "I've no more money. Cheerio."

"Cheerio, love. Take care."

THE telephone clicks off. It seems I still have some use, if only as the conveyor of spider plants. London is only a few hours by train, but it could be anywhere in the wide world. Anna is no longer daughter mine. Life has beckoned and she has gone.

Philip is standing behind me and his arms come round me, a little unsure of their welcome. He kisses the back of my neck.

"Remember me?" he says. "I live here, too."

I turn round in his arms and lean against him. Everything about him now is warm and familiar.

I am remembering before Anna, before the arrival of our much-wanted child, the hazy, almost forgotten years of our courting days when Philip

---

was so hard up; we could only go for long walks and we always seemed to have so much in common.

"There's just you and me now," he says. "It's like the beginning all over again. Only better, much better."

"Oh, Philip, you're right."

"Of course I'm right," he says. "I'm always right." And he grins, so that I know he's only teasing.

I feel the sadness of the day lifting from me. I shall see her soon and there will be so much to talk about.

Mother and daughter — friends. Certainly life has beckoned to Anna and perhaps it was beckoning to me, too.

"I wonder if Anna would mind if I borrowed her cloak?" I say a little wickedly.

"I think she would be delighted," Philip says. "Let's find it and go, Beth darling.

"You've given Anna her freedom, her choice of where to grow up and what to do. She's doing the same for you. She's handing back your time . . . you don't have to be a mother twenty-four hours of the day anymore. Now you can be yourself."

I turn and shake out the folds of my long dress and look at this man that I had almost forgotten.

This is what Anna has given back to me . . . the choice and the freedom, and something even more precious, time to be myself.

The little girl lost was not my daughter. The little girl lost was me. □

WHEN AUTUMN COMES

The morning is clear, the dew is fresh,
Autumn's arrived in her golden dress.

The leaves cascade down, without a sound,
A beautiful carpet spreads over the ground.

A hue of colours for us all to see,
It's wonderful, breathtaking, and it's all free.

As evenings grow darker, much colder too!
We think of the things we really must do.
Or just cuddle up to a log fire so bright,
Enjoying the warmth on a cold Autumn night.

At the end of the Autumn, the leaves have all gone,
Our friend the robin, will sing his song.

Our gardens are tidied, the bonfires are lit,
We all scurry round, doing our bit.

The winter will come, and then the spring,
The glorious new colours of leaves it will bring.

When Autumn leaves us, do not weep,
You can savour the memories, they are yours to keep.

Mrs M. Cripps, Pulborough.

It's Not The End Of The World

She was trying so hard to be brave, she just didn't notice that in losing "her old friend" she'd gained so many new ones . . .

IT seemed like the end of the world to Mrs Corby when she found her plant — the beautiful plant that Herbert had given her — overturned, its pot smashed and its green splendour torn and broken.

The end of the world — the end of her world, indeed.

For, as she explained to the nice policeman who came to hear her story, the plant was the last link that she had with Herbert and their lovely bungalow out Whitbury way.

The policeman listened to her story patiently; occasionally he coughed. Policemen must get so tired of asking questions and listening to long sad tales like hers.

". . . I never did like growing things indoors," she had begun. "It seems unnatural, somehow. I prefer a nice vase of flowers on the hall table, or flowers for weddings and the like . . ."

She didn't see growing things in the way that Herbert did; as if they were friends. He always liked to read about flowers and watch the gardening programmes on the telly, and think about the garden that they would have when he retired.

When he did retire they bought a bright bungalow out of Whitbury, and the garden was soon just as bright with growing colours. He was always bringing in vegetables, and great clumps of flowers.

Once he had picked four vases of sweet-william all at once so that the house smelled like the hairdressers where she used to work long ago,

IT'S NOT THE END OF THE WORLD

mplete Story by SARAH PARKES

before she had met and married him.

He was happy — so was she, with her new friends and neighbours. He liked to be alone in the garden. She liked people about her and enjoyed most of all taking the bus to Broadmead Shopping Centre to look at all the shops.

He bought the plant for her birthday. "It's called a Cheese Plant."

She thought that he must have got the name wrong but, "No, that's what the garden centre man said it was called . . ."

"Very nice, dear." She thanked him and put it on the sideboard, thinking that it would please Herbert to see it there.

And there it began to grow . . . Soon it had outgrown its little pot and needed a new one.

That was when Herbert brought stuff to make the green leaves shiny.

"Polishing leaves!" she said indignantly, but not to him. She said it to the plant — you have to talk to plants or so she'd heard someone say on the radio one day.

IT'S NOT THE END OF THE WORLD

And soon she became quite fond of it.

It grew and grew, like children do . . . It would have been nice to have had children . . .

SADLY they weren't in the pretty bungalow very long before Herbert died and the Social Services lady helped her to move into a block of flats in town. She couldn't have managed the garden on her own and was glad to be near the shops again.

Yet it was terrible that so many of her things had to be sold — she had only two rooms and a kitchenette now — but she brought all Herbert's books with her, his gardening magazines and flower encyclopaedias, and found that she was watching his gardening programmes on the telly.

By now the plant was six feet tall. Her neighbour, Mr Roberts, brought it from Whitbury in his van and it was his idea to put it on the landing outside her new front door. It was at the end of a corridor so that no-one had to walk past it.

The plant stood by the landing window looking out into the garden on rainy days.

When she came in with her shopping she always said, "Hello" and thought, sometimes, that it seemed to nod in reply . . . Well, one gets silly ideas living alone.

She liked her little flat. Her old neighbours, the Roberts, sometimes came to see her, and the lady from the Social Services. But the people in the small block weren't friendly at all.

The old couple in the next-door flat never seemed to come out of it at all. Upstairs there were foreign students and a lady with a sick baby. Then there were the schoolkids, up and down all day.

She liked children, so did Herbert, but none of these seemed to want to make friends with her at all.

She hadn't been in her new home very long when she found that two leaves had been torn off the plant outside her door. Then, another day, two more torn off the bottom, then three — torn quite viciously.

It was as if some nasty person was playing a game of "She loves me, she loves me not" slowly and deliberately, on different days. The leaves had been so green and spread out, for shade in sweltery places, Herbert had told her.

She heard children giggling on the stairs but never seemed to see them, though she looked.

She went upstairs and knocked on doors. The lady with the little sick baby came to the door crying; another was very short with her indeed and the two foreign students just looked blankly at her.

She tried to move the pot inside but it was too heavy, and besides, the plant had grown so tall.

Then one morning she went out to fetch the milk bottles in — and there it was, her plant — Herbert's plant — on the tiled floor quite smashed . . . The plastic pot was broken and the leaves lay scattered, dejected.

"I wouldn't have minded a burglary so much," she told the policeman. "You can't insure a plant, no more than you can a pet . . .

"It's the pointlessness of it that hurts. Don't the papers nowadays call it